The Sixties Boys
Rock The 70s

To Keith
Best Wish~

The Sixties Boys Rock The 70s

Alan Hammond

Foreword by Duane Eddy

© Alan Hammond 2016

First published in 2016

British Library Cataloguing in Publication Data

A catalogue record for this book is available from the British Library.

ISBN 978 1 85794 489 1

Silver Link Publishing Ltd
The Trundle
Ringstead Road
Great Addington
Kettering
Northants NN14 4BW

Tel/Fax: 01536 330588
email: sales@nostalgiacollection.com
Website: www.nostalgiacollection.com

Printed and bound in the Czech Republic

Some of the stories in the book are based on the life, experiences and memories of the author and others. Individuals shown in the photographs are not related to any of the story lines.
The band name 'Modern Edge' and compositions *Suburban Mod* and *Life is not Forever* are not meant to represent any song or band with these titles; they are purely names invented for the storyline of this book.

Contents

Front cover and title page: The band Quota Plus photographed in 1975. *F. W. Tyler*

♬ Foreword ♬

Road stories about being out there doing concerts and shows can be very interesting and sometimes hilarious. They can also be very boring because of the grinding logistics involved. A group of musicians will drive/ride all day just to play for an hour or so. Often the only good part of the day is that hour or so on stage playing our music.

Playing for the folks has always been the reason I do it. Meeting fans who often became good friends was my reward for all the travelling, sometimes bad food, uncomfortable hotels, and being exhausted. It's not always that bad, however. We do get to travel to extremely interesting places. We may only catch glimpses of them on our way to a hotel or a gig. Then again, we do get to see much of the world that many people never get to see.

Alan Hammond has told many of the stories with humour, giving you a look behind the scenes that you will seldom hear about. I could relate to some of the stories because I've done so much touring over the years myself. And I toured all over England during the late Sixties and once lived in London for several months.

I had a great band that included two members of the group named The Big Three from Liverpool: John Banks, the drummer, and John Gustafson, a great bass player, guitar player and singer who usually opened my show with a few songs.

John only played bass for me on one show when our regular bass player refused to come back on the stage. We were sharing the bill on a quite large Rock and Roll show with Bill Haley at the Albert Hall. It was full of 'Teddy Boys' and, as one of the band quipped, 'You could smell the mothballs for miles.'

I was halfway through my show and the audience was dancing in the aisles, running around and on to the stage, and in general being more wild than usual. Suddenly from the balcony behind the stage a Coca Cola bottle came flying down and hit John Banks in the back of the head, knocking him out cold. He collapsed across his drums and the song came to an abrupt halt.

We helped John backstage where he revived and began feeling better. We tried to convince him to go to the doctor but he wouldn't hear of it. He assured me he wanted to get back on stage and finish the show. I told him just to rest there for a few minutes and take it easy and wait and see how he felt later. When I saw the blood running down his head, I really got angry. I turned and went back on stage and up to the mic. I looked down at the guys milling around the aisles and generally acting like a bunch of punks. I took the mic and said loudly into it, 'Hey! I want all of you to go back to your seats and *sit – down – now*! If you don't, there'll be no more show here today. If you don't do as I say, I'm going backstage and

Duane Eddy in iconic pose.

I'm going to ask Bill Haley not to come out here at all. And,' I added, 'If any of you care, our drummer is going to be OK.'

Some looked a bit sheepish, but they all quietly went back and found their seats and sat down. It was very quiet – especially after all the noise that had been going on.

John Banks came back on stage and sat at his drums. But the bass player refused to come back. 'I don't want to take a chance on getting hit or killed,' he said.

'What am I going to do for a bass player?' I asked.

John Gus spoke up and said, 'I can play bass. I'll do it.'

When we started the music again, I was amazed. What a difference! John was so good on bass that I wanted to fire the other guy and keep John playing bass for me. But he refused. 'I really don't like playing bass all that much,' he explained. 'I really like guitar better.' So we left it at that.

I could go on and on about those great guys. They made a gruelling tour bearable. I rode with them in their van one night for several hours on our way back to London from the Midlands. I never laughed so hard in my life! They just kept a running commentary on all sorts of subjects and told jokes, and John Banks and John Gus spoke in Scouse for me. They'd grown up in that part of Liverpool and for the life of me I couldn't figure out what they were saying until they translated. It was very educational for me, not having heard it – or even heard of it – before then.

Looking back on it, I have to say those months were extremely enjoyable, difficult logistics and all. We did a couple of weeks of 'Doubles', where we'd set up in one supper-club, do our show, then pack it all up and drive like mad for 20 or 30 miles to another venue where we'd load in, set up, and do another show before we could go to our hotel and sleep.

I've travelled all over the world and played on several continents and many different countries, but my tours of England still stick in my mind and memory as some of the best ever. John Gustafson wrote to me a couple of years before he passed away and said those were some of the happiest times in his life. That certainly made me feel great.

As I said, that one hour or so every night with an appreciative audience is worth the entire lifestyle. People have always been so kind to me. I was playing in Pontypridd, Wales, on my 30th birthday. During a pause in the show, while I was getting ready to introduce the next song, someone in the audience yelled out, 'Happy birthday, Duane!'

The audience clapped and then began singing 'Happy Birthday' to me. I stood and listened and realised that what they say about the Welsh being great singers was all true. It was beautiful! I couldn't help thinking that it sounded like the Mormon Tabernacle Choir singing to me. One of those 'moments' in my life that stands out and makes it all worthwhile.

Not many people in the world get to have such a lovely experience as that was for me.

I'm sure Alan has many stories similar to this and his travels on the road have been as interesting and varied as mine have. So sit back, read his new book and see if you don't agree.

All the best
Duane Eddy

Image: Mick Phipps

♫ Introduction and Acknowledgements ♫

First of all I would like to thank everyone who bought my previous books, *The Sixties Boys*, *Sixties Boys Unzipped* and *The Sixties Boys on Tour*.

A lot of people across the country have been in touch to ask whether there were any more stories of The Sixties Boys. Well there was an era not covered in the previous books between 1969 and the mid-1970s when the boys from the Essex band Modern Edge were still chasing that elusive No 1 hit.

Living in Hornchurch, Essex, as a teenager was a great time to have lived through. The '60s and '70s were an era so different from today's world. I would like to think that the fun and humour of those years are portrayed in this book. I hope you enjoy *Sixties Boys Rock the 70ˢ*.

Many thanks go to my publisher Silver Link Publishing, and especially to Peter Townsend.

Very special thanks go to that great American legend, Duane Eddy, who has inspired many guitarists around the world and has kindly written the Foreword. He's been so helpful and is a real gentleman.

My wife Christine has been a tremendous help and support with all of my books, especially this one. She has used her skills in fine-tuning the manuscript, and added some of her own storylines. I couldn't do it without her.

I am greatly indebted to my good friends Sandra Cohen, John Clifton and Allan Stanistreet, who have checked and edited the book – they have been brilliant.

Thanks also go to Christopher Nicholson for his photographs and article.

Special thanks go to Peter Lee, David Buthlay, Ivan and Jill Bluffield, Ralph Pendry and Peter Triggs for allowing me to use their pictures.

Others in one way or another have contributed to this

publication and I would like to thank my oldest friend, Terry Page, and his wife Sandra.

One or two photographs are from people's private collections, and a reader may well recognise a photograph that they took themselves. We offer apologies in advance for not being able to credit you in person.

♫ 1 ♫

Boys of 64

It's 1969, the Kray twins are given life sentences for murder, the French Concorde made its maiden flight and Neil Armstrong, commander of Apollo 11, became the first man to set foot on the moon. Other important news is that our band, Modern Edge, has been together since 1964. We're living the dream as we play across the country and Europe to packed houses – well, nearly! Our biggest goal is to get that No 1 hit in the charts. Suddenly two early-morning phone calls changed everything overnight.

The band is made up of me, Nick Sheldon, on lead guitar, my best mate Steve on bass, Rick on keyboards, singer Ray, and a newish drummer called Billy, who's made us all go bleedin' deaf. We are in our early twenties and great mates. We've made records, played at some great venues and stayed at top hotels. It doesn't seem like that today, as we wake up at a right dosshouse of a place at the back-end of Romford Market in Essex, which the record company has rented for us. It's an old Victorian building, nicknamed 'Ponderosa', complete with outside bog. We share the place with a family of rats. If this is stardom I think I'll go back to my old job as a second-hand car salesman.

The band is sleeping in as we've played a late-night gig in the depths of Suffolk – first time we've played at a Corn Exchange. The date 1896 was on the front of the building, and from the state of the place I'd have guessed it was well before that date.

We once had roadies and soundmen to do all the hard work for us, but the record company has pulled the plug on that, so we now have our mate, Des, to do most of it. A real jack-the-lad, scruffy, looks like a scarecrow with feet at ten to two, long neck and an even longer nose, nickname 'Pinocchio' and unlucky with the birds, I wonder why, but we love him. He's the sixth member of the band.

Last night's gig was an eye-opener. We set up the gear and did a sound check, but the promoter wouldn't let us open up the curtain across the stage, so it was hit and miss as it was well dark behind there and the electrics looked right dodgy. All was revealed when the threadbare curtain opened for us to play our first set, and hundreds of moths cascaded down. We thought we were playing in the feckin' Amazon. Once the moths had settled we played our signature tune *Suburban Mod*, then went into *Venus* by the Dutch band Shocking Blue, one of my all-time favourites. It ended up a great show and one to remember.

I was the first one up the next morning after taking the two early-morning phone calls. The kitchen looked a right sorry state. All there was to drink was a jar of Camp coffee; it looked like liquid tar as I put a spoonful in my mug. Put the kettle on the gas cooker – no joy. The gas meter had run out of shillings. I had a look around to see what was to eat. Cheese with a furry coat, mottled-green sliced bread and a half-eaten apple, which could have been left over from one of the rats' breakfasts, so it was going to have to be the greasy spoon down the road at Monty's.

Second up was Rick, the keyboard player. Good looking, dark wavy hair, and even though he looked rough that morning, he still looked better than the rest of us put together – we hate him for that. He had everything, and the girl that followed him down the stairs was a darling with long blonde hair. Her knockers were fighting to get out of one of Rick's Ben Sherman shirts and there was a glimpse of black lacy knickers above the flap of the shirt. If she was mine I'd give breakfast a miss!

'What's for breakie?' he said, all cocky like.

'I ain't your batman, and who's she?'

'Meet Sofia – she's Miss Suffolk 1969.'

It had been my turn to drive the Transit to the gig last night. Steve, Des and Ray came with me. Rick and Billy took the Cortina estate and they'd brought back a couple of stunners. Well, I thought they had until Billy came down the stairs with Sofia's mate. She looked a right box of tricks. Billy is a big bloke, wears size 14 baseball boots and has a mop of untidy black hair that no comb can get through. He's not blessed with good looks and when

he talks it's like he's chewing a wasp. The bird with him was a
bit of a lump and as she walked down the stairs they creaked and
moved from side to side under the strain. She had more spots on
her face than a kid with chicken pox, and hands like shovels.

'Had a good night Billy?' I said.

'Yeah. Me and Gloria are in love.'

She looked into Billy's eyes and squeezed his hand. You could
see he was in pain as the vice-like grip took effect – she wasn't
going to let him go.

Suddenly Steve showed his face. You couldn't miss his dyed
white hair – he looked like Heinz out of the Tornados. He wasn't
happy; the girl he'd ended up with in Suffolk wasn't like that, so
there had been no nooky for him. The final band member, Ray,
had been for a run – a fit bastard, another God's gift to women,
blonde hair, blue eyes and a smile that the girls couldn't resist.

We left the girls to tidy up the hovel while we went down to
the local cafe, run by a London East End family well-known to the
police. Many a job was planned there over a full English. Des was
already there. He'd taken the Transit to his Dad's garage – a lock-
up under the arches of Romford railway station – for a check-up
before we continued our tours across the UK. His Dad was another
well-known face in the criminal fraternity. He and Des had fingers
in many pies, from property to motors, iffy to say the least.

Des was having a cup of tea with Sammy and his father Monty,
who owned the cafe. Sammy was heavy duty, in his thirties, well
over 6 foot, about 18 stone with tattoos everywhere. Des joined us
while we all acknowledged Sammy. It was best to keep in with him
– you never knew when you might need him.

While we were all together there was some bad news to share,
and I was the one to give it out. I had taken over from Tony as
spokesman and leader of the band. Tone had been our original
drummer when we first started up. Steve, Tone and I had our first
band called Tony and the Mustangs when we were at school in
Romford. Unfortunately Tone got into drugs and in 1967 he left
the band and we hadn't seen him since. Up until then we were
and still are a drug-free band. Tone's sister Penny took over the
drumming for a few months; she was brill until she got pregnant.

She had a little boy called Robin, and for sure the father is one of our band members. She won't say and no one is asking her – I wonder why. I let the band finish their artery-blocking fry-up, and while we were slurping tea it was time to give them the bad news.

'Listen up lads – we've got a few problems coming up. I've had two phone calls this morning.'

'I wondered what dick-head would ring up at 11 o'clock in the morning,' said Steve, who'd got HP brown sauce dripping out of his mouth.

'The first call was from TJ.'

'What's our manager and booker want – he knows we had a late night.'

'For Christ's sake, Steve, give it a rest and watch where you're spitting that sauce!'

'Hurry up, Nick. I've got a bird who wants my body back at the "Ponderosa",' said an impatient Rick.

'Right now, listen, and keep everything closed. TJ is moving up the ladder in the company and he won't be looking after us any more. His deputy, Julian, will be looking after us from now on.'

Interrupting and spitting out his words, Ray said, 'Not that weasel! I wouldn't trust him with my grandma's pension – he's a snake. He's only got the job because his father owns the firm. He hasn't got a clue about the music business. His nickname should be thrombosis.'

'Where did you get that from, Ray?' said Steve, laughing.

'Because he's a clot that travels around paralysing the system.'

Everyone laughed, then I said, 'The next news is even worse. Our record company is not renewing our contract. So in a month's time we won't be making any more records with them. Oh, and by the way, when our contract expires they won't be paying the rent on the "Ponderosa".'

It all went quiet until Des said, 'Don't worry about living accommodation. That can be sorted. Dad and I own a place in Upminster that'll do for the band. It's sorted, it's not a problem.'

'That's ace, Des, but what about the people living there now, and will we be able to pay the rent bearing in mind that Julian will be booking the gigs?' piped up Billy.

'It's empty at the moment, Billy – we've only just bought it. Look, you're family to me. I only have my Dad and he keeps going away on long holidays, if you know what I mean. Being with you guys is my life – whatever I can do to keep the band going, I will.'

We all went quiet and one or two of us, including me, welled up after Des's comments.

'That's great, Des,' I said. 'We owe yer. TJ has made sure we've got a few months' bookings. He doesn't like Julian either and he wanted to make sure the band stays together. He's indicated that maybe in the future he'll start up his own agency and we'll be one of the first bands he'll take on. He'll also try and get us another record deal, so all is not lost. So that No 1 hit could still be just around the corner!'

♫ 2 ♫

Trouble in Great Yarmouth

Des kept his word and we all moved into our new place in
Upminster; we kept the same nickname of 'Ponderosa'. It was right
handy as our two favourite coffee bars, La Nero and Sombrero,
were nearby. The place was down an unmade track and backed
onto fields, well out of sight. It was an old farmhouse, but with
mod cons, even an inside bog. As a bonus there was an outbuilding
where we could practise. The rent was peanuts, so everyone was
happy. We were a band that played a lot of gigs, so being under the
same roof made life easier.

My parents had died a couple of years back and I'd inherited
their small two-up, two-down in Hornchurch a few miles away.
My younger brother, Arthur, moved to Canada with his dopey
bird, Deirdre, so I was well shot of both of them. When I wanted
a bit of time alone with a girl I'd shoot home, put the Dansette
on and listen to Modern Edge's greatest hits – which took about 5
minutes! Steve and I wrote our best-selling record, *Suburban Mod*,
and that brought in a few bob in royalties, helping with the beer
and fags.

We were just settling into the new place when Des turned up
in this big American touring bus – what a beaut! The story was
that an American band had broken up after a punch-up between
themselves and their management team at an M1 services and
they needed to sell the bus to recoup some money and get back
home. Des, being Des, heard about this from a fellow roadie, made
contact, and bought it for a song, paying them in dollars. We said
we couldn't afford it and the cost of diesel would be horrendous.
Des said the price would not be an issue. When he came to sell it
he'd be quids in. He looked on it as an investment. Diesel wasn't a
problem, as he had contacts and certainly wouldn't be paying the

going rate. He did worry us because the people he and his old man ran with were heavy duty and we didn't want to get involved with anything dodgy. Famous last words!

Our next gig was in Great Yarmouth, followed by a few local gigs in the South East. After that the South West, which we called the Sunshine Tour, our favourite part of the country. In the early days, while gigging there, Steve and I met two girls, Anita and her mate Jenny from Dawlish. We saw them a number of times over the next couple of years – they were the real deal. They eventually moved away from Devon and now owned successful hair salons in Reading. Unfortunately they gave us the elbow because we weren't reliable. Couldn't blame them really. None of the band members were in long-term relationships, which made life a lot easier. Mind you, Billy was now loved up with Gloria and it was sickening listening to him going on about her.

We didn't want to deal direct with Julian, our new manager, as we'd end up lamping him one. Fortunately the company that he and TJ worked for were trustworthy and we'd never had any money issues with them, unlike some bands that have bad management and end up getting ripped off. Future bookings could be a problem once we had played our existing gigs. Steve's Dad, Tom, who worked for a solicitor, was going to take over day-to-day running of the group's accounts and making sure we didn't overspend, which we always somehow did. So now all we had to worry about was playing music, girls, parties, drinking, Woodbines and keeping out of trouble!

We set off for Great Yarmouth in our new touring bus. It was the dog's bollocks and we felt like a top band. It had everything: a toilet, kitchen and just about enough room at a pinch for all of us to sleep in. We were living the dream until the fuel gauge started going down quicker than my bank balance. We had a two-nighter at the Regal theatre, which held 400 people. For whatever reason, we were popular in East Anglia, especially here. It was fully booked for both nights, which is always nice. We played some of our own material and covers from bands like the Small Faces and the Kinks, plus a few classics like *House of the Rising Sun* by the Animals and *She's Not There* by the Zombies.

That night was one of our best for a long time – we had a ball. The audience were well behind us and we came off stage after a couple of encores. It wasn't always like that. I remember when we were playing a gig in North London for a football supporters' club. Steve sometimes can't help himself and likes to try and sing. He's had a few and starts singing West Ham's signature tune *I'm Forever Blowing Bubbles*, as they'd won that afternoon. The first chair from the audience took out the drum set and the rest of our gear was kicked all over the stage. The penny should've dropped for silly bollocks, as there were pictures of Arsenal players plastered all over the walls!

After the Yarmouth gig we were invited to a party up the road at Lowestoft. I'd had enough for one night so I gave it a miss. Des stayed with the touring bus, mind you – I think he'd pulled. While he was setting up the gear on stage the manager's daughter, Agnes, had taken a shine to our Des and started helping him lump the amplifiers in. They were a good mix, as she looked like the female equivalent of Des.

I fancied a Billy-no-mate's night. The others took the micky, but when you live in each other's pockets every day you need a break from each other. We'd played here before so I knew there was a coffee bar around the corner called Acropolis. As I was leaving the assistant manageress was leaving as well. I'd noticed her when I'd arrived. She was about my age with short dark hair and a nice smile. I did try and chat her up when she brought in a tray of coffees for the lads, but she blanked me. However, I did manage to get her name. I thought I'd try again.

'Hi, Pauline – do you fancy a coffee?'

'Thanks, Nick, but I'm meeting my boyfriend outside.'

That was that, and she'd gone. I was going to have to revamp my chat-up lines! I got myself a frothy coffee and sat down by the window. About 10 minutes later Pauline appeared and came over to me.

'He hasn't turned up, so I'll have that coffee, Nick.'

After a few minutes we're getting on really well. There was no edge to her and she had a great sense of humour. Suddenly this ugly head pressed up against the window. His eyes were bulging, steam and saliva coming out his mouth.

'Oh no, that's my boyfriend, Darren, and he gets really jealous.'

Darren stormed into the coffee bar shouting and getting aggressive. He was over 6 foot and well built and looked like a bit of a bully boy. Pauline was visibly upset – you could see she was frightened of him.

He spoke with real venom. 'Who's this knobhead, Pauline?'

'It's only Nick – he's in the band that's been playing at the Regal. When you didn't turn up, I came in for a coffee, that's all.'

'When you never showed up she ordered a taxi and she's waiting for it to come,' I said.

Pauline looked at me as if to say, what bleedin' taxi?

He grabbed her arm violently and pulled her out of the chair. I wasn't having that, so I quickly stood up and pushed him away from her. He went ballistic, but didn't try to lamp me one. I stood my ground and got brave, which is unlike me. With my strongest tough London accent, I said as I got in his face, 'You don't do that to ladies – just leave the rough stuff out or you'll have me to contend with.'

The coffee bar was full of people and went from being very noisy to complete silence. I'm saying to myself, I hope A&E is close by. I'm not a coward and I don't run away from a fight, but I like the odds to be in my favour. He was much bigger than me and he looked like he'd been in one or two punch-ups. Pauline darted between us and pulled him away from me and stood her ground, which I thought was pretty brave for a girl half his size.

Suddenly they just left. I couldn't believe it. I thought I was in for a pasting. I was out of that coffee bar in seconds in case he decided to come back. I went back to the bus parked in the theatre car park. I opened the door and thought I was in an animal enclosure. Des and his bird Agnes were making all sorts of noises as they christened the bus. It finally stopped about two in the morning.

The boys hadn't come back from last night's party, so there would be plenty of headaches when they did get back.

The next day, as Des and I walked outside in the warm early morning sunshine, they still hadn't arrived back, and alarm bells started to ring. Suddenly a police Ford Cortina Mk II screamed into the car park.

Des went white and said, 'Bleedin' hell – I wished I'd got that bus taxed and insured now.'

Two young coppers trying to look important got out of the motor and came over to us. One of them said in a strong Norfolk accent, 'Who's Nick Sheldon?'

As my bollocks dropped down to the floor I was thinking to myself, what do they want with me? I was just going to answer them when a St John ambulance pulled into the car park, and out of the back came Steve, Billy and Rick. They looked like they'd started World War Three. Looking sheepish, with bandages and plasters stuck all over them, they limped over towards the bus.

Looking at me, the copper said again, 'Are you Sheldon?'

Knowing that there was bad news coming my way, I just nodded.

'Right, first of all I would suggest getting some money out of your pocket to give to the driver of the St John ambulance who kindly delivered this rabble from the hospital.' He stared at the three walking wounded and said, 'We don't want to use the ambulance services as a taxi, do we?'

Des quickly got his wallet out and bunged the driver a pound note. The three of them nodded to the driver and mumbled their thanks.

The other copper, with a stupid grin on his mush, said, 'They were at a party and got too close to some of the local girls. Their boyfriends took exception to this. They are lucky not to be charged, not like your mate Ray Walker.'

'What do you mean?' I said.

'Didn't I tell you? One of the locals had his nose broken and is pressing charges. Looks like ABH.'

'Hang about, we've got a gig tonight, and he's our singer.'

'He won't be singing for his supper tonight. You can pick him up from the police station on the way back home to London tomorrow morning.' He then looked at Des and said, 'You look a bit shifty – what do you do in this band?'

'I'm the driver and roadie, officer.'

'That's good, because you can show me your tax, insurance and driving licence for this vehicle.'

'No problem – which one do you want to see first?'

We all looked at Des in amazement – knowing him, he probably hadn't got any of them. If there's a God, he was on our side that morning as the police radio crackled into action. There was a robbery going off at Caister and within seconds the two coppers went into overdrive and tore off out of the car park.

Back in the bus, Steve quickly told the story. 'It was a great party and the girls were lapping it up. Then the cavalry turns up in the shape of about ten locals who weren't happy, especially when Ray was upstairs with one of the bloke's birds. Then all hell lets loose – what a tear-up! As we know, Ray is an ex-ABA boxer, and he's knocking them out all over the place. The Old Bill was called but nobody wanted to take any further action except for the bloke whose bird was with Ray.'

Billy butted in, 'Yeah – we all ended up down the hospital. If you think we look bad, you should see the other lot. They're in a worse state than us.'

'It's all good news then, ain't it?' I looked at my watch and said, 'In seven hours time we've got a gig to do.'

'Leave it out! None of us are in a fit state to play, Nick,' said a moaning Rick.

'We're not letting down 400 people because you stupid idiots got in to another punch-up, so stop your bellyaching.'

Looking at the three of them, I had my doubts if we could actually put on a show, and I said to Billy, 'Besides the turban wrapped around your head, are there any other problems? Can you still play the drums?'

'I'll try, Nick, but there are six stitches under that bandage and my hands are really sore, so I won't be too heavy with the sticks tonight.'

'Well, that's a bonus,' laughed Steve.

'What about you then, laughing boy?'

'Again, hands are a bit delicate, so I'll use a pic tonight.'

I looked at Rick. He looked like the invisible man with bandages on both arms and a bleedin' great plaster above his swollen nose.

'Sorry, keyboards are out, that's for sure.'

'Right, we've got a drummer, bass and me. Rick, you'll do the singing. You were the singer in the band before you had a few months off, so I don't see that as a problem.'

'I'm up for that, Nick. Be nice to front the band again. We've been doing these numbers a while now, so I know all the words.'

'I'm going to ring Terry up to see whether he can shoot up here and help us out. He's an excellent keyboard player and guitarist.' I then looked over at Des. 'You do have all the necessary documentation for this bus?'

'Of course! Trust me, Nick – do I look like a cowboy?'

Terry was a good mate of ours out of Romford. He was a ringer for Hank Marvin of the Shadows. He was one of those talented musicians who was a multi-instrumentalist. He fronted a band called Terry and the Tanks, so called because his surname is Sherman – you couldn't make it up, could you? He did the circuit like us, so I was hoping he was at home. His Mum had to wake him up as his band had only just got back from a gig in Newcastle.

'Terry, I need your help on keyboards. Ray is locked up in a cell, the others have been involved in a punch-up and are walking wounded, and we've got a gig tonight in Great Yarmouth. Can you help?'

I thought the phone had gone dead, and I shouted to make sure he could hear me.

'Nick, I've just got home from Geordie-land after a 7-hour drive in an old Bedford van that rattled and rolled all the way home. After the gig we gave the Newcastle Brown a right hammering and you want me to drive another three hours to Norfolk?'

'That's about right – you up for it?'

'Is it the Garibaldi dance hall or the Regal theatre?'

'The Regal.'

'We played there three months ago. What time is kick-off?'

'Seven thirty, two-hour set.'

'OK, you're lucky we haven't got another gig for three days. I'll have a bit of breakie, and should be up there about three o'clock if the van don't play up.'

'I owe you mate – see you later.'

Des and I went down to the police station to try and see Ray. They wouldn't let us see him so we went straight on to the Regal. As we walked and hobbled into the theatre the manager couldn't believe his eyes. He laughed and said, 'The feckin' panto season finished three months ago, lads.'

We got in there earlier than normal. With Rick singing we needed to write a new set list and play some of the songs to make sure he was up to speed. As it happens it went well and everyone did their bit to make sure the punters had a night to remember. We were having a break when Pauline came in. She looked tasty with her mini-skirt and tie-dyed pink shirt. I made a beeline for her; I was worried about what her boyfriend might have done to her.

'Pauline, you OK?'

'I'm fine, Nick. I've just come to say thanks for sticking up for me last night.'

'That's not a problem I was really worried about you when you left the coffee bar. It's not for me to say, but why do you put up with a bloke like that?'

'I've told him I don't want to see him any more, but I don't think he'll take no for an answer, so I'm a bit worried about that.'

Terry wouldn't be here for another hour or more, so I suggested a walk along the seafront, which she readily agreed to. I didn't realise what a nice genuine girl she was and we got on really well. She wanted to move to London to get a job in the music industry. Her problem was that she lived with her Dad; he was an invalid and relied on her a lot, and there weren't any other family members to look after him. As we were getting on so well together, I asked if she would like to spend the rest of the day with us and come to the gig. She was up for that, as she wasn't on duty today. I was as happy as Larry as we held hands and walked back to the Regal.

Terry arrived, and as soon as he saw the boys he started winding them up. Billy was first.

'I thought I was on the set for *Emergency – Ward 10*, Billy. I like the head gear – when yer off to India, then?'

'Piss off, Terry. What band would call themselves Terry and the Tanks?'

Then it was Rick's turn, 'They'll be no wanking tonight, Rickie boy. But there's a bonus.'

'What's that then, silly bollocks?'

'Least the audience will have a proper keyboard player tonight. Steve, you still playing that bass guitar with one finger?'

'Do you know, Terry, you're giving me the arse ache and you've only been here a minute.'

Terry noticed Des's bird, Agnes, as she went off to get some tea for us. 'Christ, Des, is there another Battersea Dogs Home nearby.'

Pauline was shocked as she listened to the banter and said, 'Is it always like this, Nick?'

'Yeah, sorry about this but they love each other really.'

After the wind-ups, we were back on song and got down to some serious rehearsing. Terry knew most of the numbers already and he fitted in well. We always dressed in white Fred Perry shirts and sta-prest trousers, but tonight it was anything we could fit into. We looked like a cross between the Undertakers and the Pirates.

With about an hour to go, we were all in the dressing room with Pauline and Agnes, having a sandwich and a beer, when we had a right shock. Our new manager, Julian, turned up. He was about 40, receding hair, old-fashioned check suit and definitely batted for the other side. In his posh Chelsea accent he sneered, 'Is this who I'm representing? I can't believe you are going out on stage looking like that.'

'We're a bleedin' rock band, not a classical chamber music group,' said Steve.

'There's no need for that type of language.'

'Are you real, Julian? Look out there tonight. It's full, people like our music, and they don't care what we look like.'

'Don't get smart with me, sonny. I know your singer is in jail and that is not good publicity for our company. I don't see us renewing your contract when it's up in a few months' time.'

'Well, that's fine by us,' I said. 'There are other people who'd want us on board. We ain't losing any sleep about that, so on your way and close the door after you. We've got a gig to play.'

Julian stood there for a second, lost for words, then rushed out of the room like a scalded cat. Rick then said, all jokey, 'Well, that told him, Nick. By the way, who are the other people who want us?'

'I ain't got a bleedin' clue.'

Pauline and I popped outside so I could have a quick drag. I laughed as I said, 'Listening to our manager and seeing what goes on behind the scenes, do you still want to get involved in the music business?'

'Even more so. I'd certainly treat acts much better than he does.' She then gave me a cuddle and a kiss and said, 'Especially you, Nick.'

You'd have to play in a band to understand how special it is to go on stage and play to an audience. Tonight was no exception. As we entered the stage we got an enthusiastic applause. Billy went and sat behind his Ludwig drum set. He'd put a pork-pie hat on top of his turban to try and hide it, but it didn't work – he looked a right wally. Rick, with all his bandages and plasters, was having difficulty holding the 'Sure' microphone. In the end he had to put it in a mic stand. It was funny seeing Terry behind the Farfisa keyboard instead of Rick. He had this stupid grin and, looking like Hank Marvin, you can't help but laugh. Steve plugged in his Gibson bass and I adjusted my Fender guitar. Funnily enough, when you have a new band member it gives you that added edge. It all went well and when we'd finished the last number of the first set and walked back into the dressing room, there was a despondent Ray and Des having a chat.

'They've let you out then, jailbird?'

'Yeah, Steve, it's not funny. I'm mullered – the bastards have charged me with ABH. The geezer I whacked wants his pound of flesh. I'm on bail awaiting a court appearance. What pees me off is that him and his mates started it. And another thing, I can't go out of the country, so there's no gigging for me abroad till the case comes to court, which could take ages.'

I've known Ray for a few years and he's a tough cookie, but I could see that he was well choked up and maybe he thought his life on the road was coming to an end.

After the gig I walked Pauline home, which wasn't far from the theatre. We were like a courting couple as we giggled and stopped for a few snogs along the way. Every bird you meet is special for a night or two, but she was a bit more than that, especially with her apple blossom perfume ramping up the juices. As we entered her road she suddenly stopped, grabbed hold of me and looked frightened as she said, 'Darren's outside my house in his van waiting for me. I told him I don't want to see him any more. Nick, don't get involved, please. I'll go in at the back of the house.'

'You sure?'

'Yeah, I'm fine, Nick. Thanks for a great day and it was lovely meeting you. You will ring me when you get back home?'

'Promise.'

I held her tight and kissed her goodnight. I didn't want to let her go – I was really worried about her. I made sure that she got back into her house safely. She turned and waved goodnight to me. As I made my way back I passed Darren's van, which had the name of his electrical company on it. For a second I thought I'd get involved, but it might have made it worse than it was. Hopefully, after a few days he would move on, so I let it be.

♫ 2 ♫

Don't mess with Monty

The next couple of weeks we were playing nearly every day. Fortunately they were local bookings in Essex and Kent, so there was not a lot of travelling. There was a cloud over the band with Ray's pending court case. The fun had gone out of our playing and we all got a bit edgy with each other. We did get a brief for him so he'd be well represented in court.

I'd been phoning Pauline every other day and she sounded really down. Her ex was still giving her grief. One of our gigs got cancelled so I had the day off and went and saw her. She was pleased to see me and we had a great day together. She'd lost weight and you could see by her face that this Darren was getting to her. He'd been stalking her and kept ringing and turning up at odd hours. I suggested she should go to the police, but she was scared of the consequences. Her father was not a well man and he couldn't physically help – it was starting to affect him as well. I felt useless that I couldn't help as I lived 3 hours away. When we said our goodbyes she broke down and cried and just held onto me. Something had to be done. When I got back home Des phoned to say he wanted to see me at Monty's cafe tomorrow morning. He knew that I had gone to Yarmouth to see Pauline and I told him about the problems she was having with this Darren. He listened and said he'd see me tomorrow.

As I walked into the cafe he was there with Ray. We sat down at a table in the corner and ordered our tea and bacon sarnies. I've known Des all my life. He had a tough upbringing. He's loyal and would do anything for you. But he does have an edge and mixes with people who you wouldn't like to upset. It's best not to ask too many questions about what he gets up to when he's not with the band. He's one of those blokes that when he speaks you listen, and this morning was no exception.

He said with a chill in his voice, 'We all know we've got a problem with this bloke who's broken the code of silence and should've kept schtum – instead he's told the police about the fight with Ray. Everybody including his own mates has kept quiet about the fight and moved on, but this bloke has now jeopardised the band by opening his mouth. So he's got to be told verbally or physically that this ain't going to happen.'

A worried Ray butted in. 'What do you mean, physically?'

'We'll use whatever methods are needed, Ray. I can assure you that the guys who do this are pros. Once he meets them he'll withdraw the allegations.'

'But what happens if he doesn't?'

'This team has a hundred per cent success rate, Nick. And while they're in Norfolk they'll pay a visit to this bloke who's giving Pauline grief. You got any info on him?'

'I know the name of the electrical company he works for.'

'That's all I need.' He laughed and said, 'We'll give him a shock when we turn up. Any problems before I set this up?'

'Who's going to pay for all this?'

'Don't worry about that, Nick – in my world we help each other. You both OK with this?'

'Well, I am – I don't won't to go to prison,' said a worried Ray.

'Nick, how about you?'

'Yeah, I'm in – he's a menace and needs to be sorted.'

'OK. I don't want you saying anything to anybody, not any of the other band members and of course not to Pauline.'

'When will all this happen?'

'Best you don't know, Nick.'

Des left us and went to another table where Monty was sitting with a couple of his associates. Monty was in his sixties, short and stocky with piercing blue eyes, a real hard nut. I'd hate to upset him.

Ray and I went back to my place to have a chat about our meeting with Des. Ray was really worried in case it all went pear-shaped and the police came down on him again.

We had a gig later that day in Chelmsford, which would help take our mind off things. It was somebody's engagement party – we didn't normally do that type of gig, but the money was good and it was only up the road. We all met up at our new 'Ponderosa' in Upminster to load up the gear. Ray and I thought we were the first ones there and had a cup of tea in the kitchen. Then Ray said to me, 'Can you hear running water, Nick?'

'Yeah I can – I hope we ain't got a leak.'

A few minutes later it sounded like the feckin' sinking of the *Titanic*. Water started coming down through the ceiling. Ray and I ran up the stairs and went into the bathroom. The door was ajar and we couldn't believe our eyes. I've never had sex in the bath and after witnessing this I never want to. Billy was on top of Gloria giving it an enormous amount of welly. Water was going everywhere. Imagine it, 30-odd stone splashing about in a bath that was too small for one of them, let alone two. Ray and I couldn't stop laughing and had to go back downstairs.

When it was all over and the tide had gone out, they came down the stairs like nothing was wrong. She was now living with Billy in our place and that was starting to cause friction in the band. I could see trouble ahead. We'd all agreed that while we all lived together no girls were going to stay on a permanent basis. Billy also informed us that she was coming to all the gigs.

We arrived at this posh hotel in Chelmsford and took the gear in. Des had said no more about our meeting and just got to work setting up the Vox 30 amps and the rest of the equipment on stage. The gig was in this massive ballroom, and there was bunting everywhere – somebody must have spent hours blowing up hundreds of balloons, as they hung in a net above the ceiling. A very pretty girl came over to see us – it was her engagement party. Samantha was about 20 with striking long black hair, a figure to die for and a well-cultured posh voice. You might call her the thinking man's crumpet, or did she fancy a bit of rough? She explained what was going on and how she wanted the evening to go, which was fine by us. Her fiancé, Giles, who was in his mid-20s, then turned up. What a tonker! He was tall and thin with thick black rimmed glasses and a voice that oozed money. In his eyes we were servants and had to obey his every wish. We took no notice of him and he moved on to bore some other poor sod. Now

Samantha had our full attention. Rick had gone quiet and made eye contact with her. She tried to look away but kept flicking her eyes towards him. Oh, no! I've seen that look before from Rick. I was glad we'd got the money up front.

There were about 150 guests in the ballroom, most of whom looked toffee-nosed. We started playing, but unfortunately it wasn't going to be our night. This Samantha kept coming over to Rick, fluttering her eyelashes at him. It was her engagement party – I couldn't believe it. You knew it was all going to end in tears and it did. After the first set Rick and Samantha disappeared. Her fiancé went looking for her and found them having a grope.

Steve had the final say at the party. On the side of the stage where he was playing there was a switch that had a piece of cellophane over it saying 'Do not touch'. Steve has always been an inquisitive bastard – he can't help himself. I remember when he was at school there was a kid in our class nicknamed Wiggy. He had a mop of black hair and everybody thought it was a syrup. One day Steve pulled this poor kid's hair. The screams echoed around the school. For his troubles Steve got six of the best on his arse from headmaster Mr Morgan's favourite cane.

Anyway, he'd been looking at this switch all night and the inevitable happened. Just before the second set he took the paper off this switch and pulled it. In slow motion hundreds of balloons floated down on top of the guests. It was pandemonium with a lot of upset people and a fiancé who was after Rick's blood, so it was an early bath for us. I didn't think we'd be doing the entertainment at the wedding.

Bolton girls do like a roadie

Over the next few weeks everything that could've happened, happened. The funniest moment was at a gig in Bolton. It was a long journey up there so when we arrived we were knackered, especially as the night before we'd had a party at the new 'Ponderosa'. As we got off the bus there were three girls waiting for us. We didn't have many groupies chasing us – they were usually after the top A bands, but we were somewhere between B and Z, which meant that we'd take what was on offer. As soon as the band got off the bus, the best-looking one of the three said with a sexy voice, 'Who's the singer?'

Now, there's a pecking order when these girls want a bit of your body. It starts off with the singer, then lead guitarist, and so on. This was a first for all of us and we looked at each other and grinned.

I said, 'He's still in the bus, luv.'

With that she jumped in the bus and shut the door. We shared a Woodbine with the other girls, who made it quite clear we weren't on their list! About 15 minutes later the girl jumped out of the bus with a smile that told you she'd got her trophy, and off they walked. The door opened again and there was Des, looking as happy as a dog with two dicks. He must've thought it was Christmas, because he normally only got the leftover's from Crufts.

It was the first time we'd played here. It was a nice theatre and the staff couldn't do enough for us, which included getting well fed. We were happy bunnies as we hit the stage and plugged in. After last-minute checks I looked at Billy to drum us in for the first song when all hell let loose. The girl who'd made Des happy was in the front row with her mates. When she saw our singer Ray she stood up and went off her head, shouting and screaming that he

wasn't the real singer and where was he? Des was doing the sound
for us on the side of the stage and as soon as he heard her go off
he tried to hide behind the sound unit. She clocked him and the
penny dropped that her trophy had been a roadie, which in her
book was bottom of the pile. She tried to get on stage to kill Des,
but fortunately security got hold of her and dragged her outside.
After the gig we were out of there, pronto. Des drove out of the car
park like a maniac, and I couldn't see him going back to Bolton
again.

There was a nice outcome for Ray when we got back home.
Surprise, surprise, Ray's brief, Mr Goldberg, called him to say that
the police would be dropping all charges against him regarding
the ABH. I wonder how that happened? I was still in touch
with Pauline on a regular basis. During the last couple of phone
calls she had never mentioned her ex, Darren, and seemed a lot
happier. I rang her when I got home and asked if she was having
any more trouble with him. No, she wasn't, but when she was in
town a couple of days ago she'd seen him on the other side of the
road. He had a bad limp and his hand was in a sling.

'He must've had an accident,' I said.

Ray and I did ask Des about what happened, and all he said
was, 'The ABH bloke had agreed it was a good idea not to give
evidence against Ray, and the case was dropped. Darren, Pauline's
former boyfriend, got a bit brave, but soon came around to our way
of thinking.'

The inevitable happened. Julian, our manager, took great
delight in telling Tom, Steve's Dad, that our contract would not be
renewed in three months' time. He didn't have the bottle to front
us up with the news. We tried to get in touch with our previous
manager, TJ, but he'd left Julian's father's company quite suddenly.

When you're in your early twenties and having fun making
music, you can easily forget that without the money coming in you
haven't got a band. None of us wanted the dream to end and there
would have to be measures put in place until hopefully another
company would pick us up. After having a chat with Tom it was
agreed that we would cut our cloth accordingly. We moved out
of the 'Ponderosa' in Upminster straight away. I think Des was

happy about that because his Dad had other ideas for the property, which we won't go into! We all had alternative places to live, mostly with family members, and I had Mum and Dad's house. Tom allowed us to store the musical kit in his very large garage, which also stored his pride and joy, a 1932 Morris Eight. He made it quite clear that we didn't go anywhere near it when loading and unloading the equipment. The touring bus went – Des had an offer on it, which he couldn't refuse. So it was back to the Transit. We felt like we were starting up the band all over again, which in a way we were.

We were off on tour to the South West in a few days time, but before that it was the anniversary of the death of brother and sister Rod and Carol and our mate Jimmy – all three had died in 1964. They'd been great friends of ours since our early school days. Carol was a great girl and we'd been out a few times, but nothing serious. They'd tragically died in a car accident. Each year the gang that we knocked about with would meet up and lay flowers on their graves at Crow Lane, Romford. There was Anne and Diane, with whom I had a little fling. I still fancied her, but she'd moved on, which was a shame. Alec, who was the ace face of the Mods in Essex in 1964, still had a Lambretta with loads of mirrors and lights on it. With his fishtail parka and pork-pie hat he did look the business. Wendy and Roger were there, and also Ronnie, a bit of a rascal who could get you anything. We would have dealings with him later. As we laid the flowers we had a moment to reflect on how life is so precious and how suddenly it can come to an end. We later went back to the La Nero coffee bar in Hornchurch where our friendships had begun. Mind you, nothing had changed as I still got lumbered with paying for the frothy coffees for everybody!

♫ 5 ♫

Not a good start to the Sunshine Tour

It sounds great when you say to people you're going on tour, but there is a down side to it all. Living in dodgy bed and breakfasts, Steve's stinking feet, Billy's farting, Ray gets hay fever and is always sneezing and sniffing. Then there's Rick, who has this habit of scratching his nuts, which always happens when he comes back from meeting a bird.

Nothing runs smooth and it started even before we left. Billy and his Gloria were now a couple and he wanted her to come on tour with us. Well, she wasn't coming in the van, and the group's Ford Cortina estate was our transport. Billy got the arse ache and kicked off. Now, we knew Gloria had some form of transport but we didn't know what it was. It was unusual, as ladies hardly ever had their own car, let alone being able to drive. So it was agreed they would follow behind us in her motor.

We were ready to go to our first gig in Reading. Des was driving the Transit and Steve was up front in the Cortina. We put the eight-track on with Spencer Davis blaring out from the speakers. But there was no Billy and Gloria until Ray shouted out, 'What the feck's that?'

In the distance we could see this three-wheeler chugging towards us. As it got nearer we were crying with laughter. There was Mr and Mrs Billy Bunter sitting in this bright yellow Trojan bubble car. As it pulled up Billy got out of the front of it, with some difficulty, and said, 'Cool, ain't it, lads?'

We wet ourselves with laughter, then after this side show we were off to Reading. Rick looked behind us at the bubble car and said, 'It's like we're being followed by a feckin' wasp.'

We were playing at the Town Hall, which was a nice venue. We arrived early and there was plenty of local help to unload the gear and set up.

I made sure that I rang Pauline in Yarmouth before I left home. I didn't want her ex hassling her. She said he'd gone off the radar and everything was fine except her Dad, who wasn't too well, and she was worried about him. I said that as soon as I got back I'd visit her.

We had a couple of hours before the sound check so Steve and I went to a certain hair salon not too far away. As mentioned, we had met Anita and Jenny back in the mid-'60s down in Devon. We were close to both of them until about 18 months ago, when they knocked us into touch. We couldn't blame them as we were always travelling about and they got fed up with the lack of commitment from us. They went back to their former boyfriends, two toffee-nosed ex-public schoolboys who spoke with a plum in their gob. They were well-known rugby players in the area, their families had loads of money, and they both had good jobs. The girls had great delight in telling us about them when they jacked us in. Anita and Jenny had done well for themselves, opening up a couple of hair salons, so fair play to them. If the girls think we're not good enough for them now, so be it. In our world we've done well and are having fun – it certainly ain't boring. I still care about Anita – she was a really special girl. Perhaps if I'd been older and more mature I would've settled down with her. I suppose it's my loss and I might come to regret it later on in life. After all this, we still thought we'd go to the salon that they owned and say hello to them. We knew the manageress, Shelly, and some of the stylists. Being full of ourselves, we thought we'd just bounce in and they'd be all over us.

I opened the door and shouted out to the girls in the salon, 'Have you missed us, girls?'

Well, it was like a death in the family. They looked at Steve and me like we were the grim reapers. Shelly quickly came over to us and said curtly, 'Sorry, you're both banned.'

'What do you mean, banned?' said Steve.

Shelly took us outside the shop and said, 'Look, I'm really sorry. Anita and Jenny thought you'd come into the shop today as you're playing in town. They've said you're not welcome in the shop and not to bother them again.'

We were speechless. Banned from a hairdressers – that's got to be a first. Shelly put her hand on my arm and said gently, 'Anita and Jenny are not the girls you used to know. Unfortunately they're hardnosed business ladies and have gone all snobby, which doesn't suit them. Ever since they met Simon and Rupert their attitude and arrogance has rubbed off on to the girls. I'm really sorry.'

'Well, there ain't a lot more to say, Shelly. I'm really sorry it's come to this as there was never any bad blood between the four of us.'

'Look, Nick, all the girls are coming to the gig tonight and we're looking forward to seeing you guys play. After the show we've booked a small room at the pub opposite the town hall. A couple of the girls have just qualified as stylists and the salon is having a drink to celebrate their success, so come and join us.'

'What about Rag, Tag and Bobtail – aren't they coming?'

'What, Anita and Jenny?'

'Yeah.'

Shelly starts giggling and says, 'No, Steve, they're going to a show in London with the rugby club. I don't see them coming back to a staff party – that's below them now.'

'I can't see Jenny going out with a Rupert. What a dick of a name that is.'

'Well, his parents are millionaires and have bought him a luxury flat by the river, so that helps.'

We met up with the lads and had a sound check. Everything was in place for a good night. It was going to be jam-packed, so there should be a buzz.. About an hour before the show TJ, our former manager, bounced into the dressing room. He was in his mid-30s with long black hair and dressed in a colourful military uniform. We'd met him in Reading when he was promoting bands back in the mid-'60s and later we joined the company he worked for. He was a good bloke and you could trust him, which in this industry is a bonus.

'Hiya, lads – do you like the outfit?'

'You're off to Vietnam then?'

'Oh piss off, Ray – this is Carnaby Street gear, mate.'

'More like army surplus store.'

TJ noticed Billy and Gloria in the corner of the room and shouted out, 'Billy, I didn't know they had women bouncers here.'

Fortunately Billy had his tongue down Gloria's throat, so he didn't cotton on.

'Right, listen up. In a couple of months' time my agency will be up and running, and knowing you've just been elbowed out from Julian's mob I want you on board. As you know I've left the company but my contract with them states that I can't start my agency for three months. I've got an office in Frith Street in the West End and I'm looking for staff right now. How's that grab yer, lads?'

'Top man – can't wait to get on board,' I said.

All the boys nodded except Des, who looked a bit worried.

'What about me? Am I part of all this?'

'Of course, Des – you save us a fortune in diesel! Seriously, Modern Edge wouldn't be a band without you. By the way, I saw Tone last week.'

'What, our former drummer?' Steve said.

'Yeah he's off the drugs and playing with a band in Kent. He sends his regards to you all. He's better than bongo Billy. Look at him – where did he find her?'

Billy was oblivious to what he was saying as he was now locked in a bear hug. TJ left his card and said he'd be in touch nearer the time to sort out contracts. He was out as quick as he came in. As he went out this gorgeous bird in a micro mini-skirt came in with two plates of sandwiches. She placed one plate on the table, then went over to Rick and gave him the second plate. She then said to him, in a really sexy voice, 'You've got the ham off the bone special and they've got the cheese. See you after the gig by the stage door. I'll have the Mini running and we'll go back to my place.'

'How do you do that?' said Steve with a sneer.

'You've either got it or you ain't. Petra just happens to have great taste.'

'Have you told her about the spots around your old boy?' says Ray.

'You wouldn't … would you?'

'Your secret is safe with me as long as we get the ham off the bone sarnies!'

This venue had a great atmosphere and as we got on stage the welcome was as good as it gets. The girls from the salon were standing in the front and you could see they were in a party mood. Tonight we were playing a few more covers besides our own material. We'd learned a few new numbers and we started off with two of them: *Lady Madonna* by the Beatles and *Itchycoo Park* by the Small Faces. The sweat was pouring off of us as we got stuck into the first set. The second set was just as good, and we finished the night on a real high. We didn't have to pack the gear up until the morning, and we had a bed and breakfast within walking distance, so everything was sweet. Steve and I shot over to the pub to see the girls.

There were about 30 people there and everybody made us welcome. The girls from the salon said how much they had enjoyed the show, which is always nice. With plenty of drink and food on offer we were looking forward to finishing the night off in style. As the music played from the Dansette record player, Shelly and I had a nice smooch to *A Whiter Shade of Pale* by Procol Harum. Steve got close to Josie, one of the stylists, so we were both happy. After about 45 minutes, everything went quiet. Shelly unlocked herself from me and looked over to the doorway. Standing there with faces like thunder were Anita and Jenny, done up like a dog's dinner with their rugby front row forwards. There were also another two couples with their muscle-bound boyfriends. Anita stepped forward and tore into Shelly while looking at us two.

'What are these two doing here? This is a staff function that the salon is paying for. I told you they're not welcome.'

'I invited them here – what's the problem with that?'

Then Jenny had her say. 'The problem is, Shelly, that you've disobeyed our orders, that's what's wrong.'

Shelly was visibly upset, as were the other stylists. I couldn't help myself.

'What's the problem with you two? You never used to be like

this. You're acting like a couple of tyrants.'

Then it all went wrong. Simon, Anita's bloke, who was built like a brick built shit house, piped in, 'Don't talk to my girlfriend like that.'

'Oh, leave it out, will yer?' I said.

Then Rupert, the other brick built shit house, had his say. 'And that goes for me as well with Jenny.'

Steve got into Rupert's face and snarled, 'Your parents must have feckin' hated you to call you Rupert.'

All hell broke loose as Simon and Rupert started to throw punches at us. We somehow blocked them and landed a couple back. The next thing we knew, they and their two mates got hold of us and gave us a couple more punches, then threw us out the front door. The pub bouncers, who'd heard the commotion, saved us from maybe more damage. Anita and Jenny came outside to see us and looked really shocked. Then Shelly and Josie rushed out and came over to see us.

Shelly turned on Anita and let her have it. 'You two have gone too far this time. You can poke your job – most of the other stylists hate your guts as well!'

We could hear police sirens, so Steve and I left in case they were coming our way. We felt like wimps as we limped up the road.

The next morning as we loaded the gear into the van, we still couldn't get over it. We told the guys what had happened, and they were gutted that they hadn't been there to help us. Ray knew the girls well, as did the other members of the band.

He said, 'That's not the Anita and Jenny I know. They're great girls. I'll tell you what the problem is – they're in denial. They've still got the hots for you two.'

'Got a bleedin' funny way of showing it,' I said.

We wondered where Rick was until the venue manager said that there'd been a phone call for us. It was Rick – he was having a lie in with Petra and would meet us in Swindon that night for the gig. He was a jammy bastard – he always got out of humping the gear about.

Halfway to Swindon we got a puncture in the Cortina. It was pouring down with rain, the spare was flat and there was also a

leak from one of the windows at the back of the van. Water was
dripping onto one of the amps so it needed to be shifted. It was
times like this that you said to yourself, why am I doing this? We
somehow got to a lay-by and just sat there thinking it ain't going
to mend itself. The wasp turned up and Gloria and Billy jumped
out. Gloria surprised us all when she said enthusiastically, 'What's
the problem, lads?'

'Got a puncture and the spare is flat,' I said.

'I'll get that sorted. Where's the spare?'

I pointed to where it was. She picked up the wheel in one
hand and put it on the front seat of the bubble car, revved up and
she was away. Within an hour she was back and started changing
the wheel. We looked on in amazement as she got stuck in – she
looked like she'd been doing this all her life. She overheard us
talking about the leaky window, so after changing the wheel she
said, 'Show me this leaky window.'

Des showed her where it is. She had a good look and asked Des
for a flat screwdriver. After a few minutes of fiddling around, she
cracked the bottom seal with the handle of the screwdriver and
said triumphantly, 'That will fix it.'

'Where'd you learn all this?' I said.

'My Dad owns a garage. I've always helped him – learned quite
a bit on the way.' With a grin on her face, she added, 'There's more
to me than just being good in bed.'

Well, I've never seen six blokes so dumbfounded when she
came out with that. Girls never said anything like that. Billy
was lost for words and just looked at her in amazement. Gloria
added, 'I've known you lot for a few weeks and you think I'm
dumb and stupid, all of you except Billy. I've had to be crude to
get your attention. I might not be the prettiest of girls and yes, I'm
overweight, but it's about time you treated me as the person I am,
not what I look like.'

'You're right, Gloria. We've been well out of order and
prejudged you. Please accept our apologies. By the way, can you
repair our eight-track that's playing up too? Your first statement –
is that true?' I said.

She looked at me and grinned. 'You'll never know, will you,

Nick? I accept your apologies and I'll have a look at the eight-track when we're in Swindon.'

As we neared the outskirts of Swindon all we could see were posters for one of the biggest bands on the planet. Looking closer, they were playing here tonight. What a cock-up – we've got no chance of anyone turning up for our gig. This had happened here before. We ended up with all the drop-outs and psychos. It was a nightmare and it always ended in trouble at this venue. The place was second-rate – everything about it was dingy and run down.

We set up and Gloria, now my favourite lady, popped out to the fish and chip shop for us all. I was just eating my rock eel and chips when Rick decided to show his face. He walked in looking a million dollars with his bird, Petra, who was drop dead gorgeous. He looked at his bird and said with a grin, 'I'm sorry I'm late, lads – you know what it's like.'

'No, I don't know what it's like,' growled Ray.

'Oh, by the way Rick,' said Steve. 'Your wife phoned. The twins have got chicken pox, but there's good news – she's expecting your third child.'

'What're you on about, Steve?' said Rick.

Petra then went into one, slapped Rick around the mush, kicked him in the cobblers and stormed out, nearly taking the door off its hinges.

Rick had one hand on his nuts and the other rubbing his cheek. 'What's that all about, lads?'

'I'll tell you what it's all about, Rick,' I said. 'We're pissed off unloading the gear, setting up at the gigs and sorting out all the other problems like getting soaking wet changing a tyre while you're shagging. If you ain't going to do your share you can sling your hook.'

Rick looked at all the band and they all nodded their heads. 'You don't mean it, Nick.'

'I bleedin' well do.'

'You're all jealous of me.'

'No, we're not jealous, Rick, we've just had enough. Now we ain't got any roadies any more, we all have to lump in. It's take it or leave it time – up to you.'

'Well, I don't want to leave the band.'

'Fine. Now that's sorted, go and get the teas – there's two sugars in mine,' I said.

As Rick walked out looking dejected, the owner of the place wormed his way in. We knew him from old. He was in his sixties, unshaven, dressed like a tramp with a personality of a sewer rat.

'Hello, lads – nice to see you again.'

'I wish I could say the same thing about you,' piped up Steve.

'We've got a couple of problems tonight, lads. Because the headline band is in town the gate money will be well down, which in turn means we won't be able to pay the contract price. Plus it's a sad night tonight as this is the last show here as they're knocking the place down. I've sold it to a builder.'

Now, we don't get involved with contracts and the money side of the business – that's done through our management. But tonight was to be an exception. This bloke was a snake and I don't see any money coming our way once he'd closed the doors for the last time. A lot of the gigs you get the money up front, but not here. So action needed to be taken.

'Squiby, we've known you a fair while. It has to be said that I wouldn't trust you with a church collection box.'

'That's a bit strong, Nick.'

'Look, money up front or no music.'

'OK, no music if you're going to be like that.'

'That's fine by us. We hate playing here – it's a dosshouse for all waifs and strays. Right, let's go and get the gear off the stage, boys, and put it back in the van.'

As we walked out of the dressing room he shouted out, 'OK, I'll pay you.'

'Get the contract that our company sent to you and we'll see what we've got to collect.'

Squiby slid back in like an eel and gave me the contract. I looked at it and noticed that the top of the page was bent over by about an inch. I peeled it back and it said May 1968. It was the previous contract with us.

'You can't help yourself, can you, Squiby?'

'What do you mean?'

'Do we look like we've got carrots on top of our heads? Go and get the 1969 contract before we get the right arse ache.'

He disappeared and came back with the right paperwork. 'Who shall I make the cheque out to, Nick?'

I've never heard so much laughter from one question. Billy moved forward, fronted Squiby up and sneered, 'Do we look divvy? Pound notes. Do I make myself crystal?'

'Pound notes. You're having a laugh.'

'Well, make it fivers then.'

I was now not happy and I lost my temper. 'I hate this place! I poxy hate you even more for trying to stitch us up. You've got 5 minutes to get the readies or we're walking – no, in fact running out of here. Now, get out of my sight, you weasel, and get the money.'

He disappeared and within minutes he was back with the cash.

'Can I have a receipt, please?'

That was the second biggest laugh of the night. Ray went for a pee and looked into the dance hall on the way back to see how many punters were in there.

'Do want the good news or the bad news?' he said.

'Good news first,' said Rick, who had come back with a tray of lukewarm tea.

'The good news is, it's nearly full.'

'What's the bad news then?' said Des.

'It's full of Rockers.'

'Oh no, just what we didn't want. Right plan B. Let's get moving,' I said.

We're a Mod band so Rockers can cause us trouble. We'd had this before, so we knew what we had to do. First we took some of our amps off the stage and used the venue's PA system. It was not a good sound but we had to protect our equipment. We changed the set list to put more heavy numbers in. We went from Mod target tee-shirts to plain black ones. Steve and I changed our guitars to back-up ones, which were copies of my Fender and Steve's SG Gibson bass. Steve and I stayed in the dressing room sorting out our guitars while the other guys beavered away on stage.

There was a knock on the door, and a bouncer came in and

said, 'There are two girls out here who want a quick word with some band members. Can I let them in?'

Normally it was a straight yes, the more the merrier, but tonight it was all hands to the pumps. Steve then said, 'OK, but just for a minute.'

We had the shock of our lives. Standing there were Anita and Jenny. Jenny said, 'Can we have a word with you both about last night?'

Steve stepped in and said, 'No, you can't. Last night was well out of order, not just with us but poor Shelly. We don't want aggro like that. You're not nice to know any more.'

I then had my say. 'We've known you two for a long time and whatever we are or have been there has never been any nastiness between us.'

'Look, Nick...'

'No, you look, Anita. There was a time when I was in love with you and Steve felt the same about Jenny. We know we messed up, but what occurred last night with you and your other halves was nasty. You took great delight in telling us when we split up that you'd moved on from us. As far as I'm concerned I don't want to talk or see you again, so just leave.'

'Do you feel the same way, Steve?'

'Yeah, I'm with Nick. You've changed, Jenny, and you're not nice to know any more. Your world is not our world, so I suggest we leave it at that.'

They stood there for a second and I saw tears in Anita's eyes. They left and Steve looked at me and said sadly, 'It's really sad it's come to this, but...'

We had no more time to think as the others charged back in and we got ready for the gig. There was no stage, so we weren't protected from any unhappy revellers. We somehow got through the first set, but for the second set we weren't quite so lucky. In 1969 there weren't too many problems with Mods and Rockers – that had fizzled out in the mid-'60s. But there was a comeback tonight. A bunch of Mods came in for the second half and wanted more than a dance. It didn't take long before the first chair was thrown. We went into overdrive – amps and the other gear were out the back door into the van in record time.

Within half an hour we were off to our B&B in South Wales. I don't know why we play Wales. For whatever reason they don't like us there, but we don't book the gigs. Last time we played here Steve, being drunk, said to the audience that besides shagging sheep there wasn't a lot else to do there. The night was no better than when we had last played here – it was crap and we played crap, so we got out of town as quickly as possible.

The next morning we were heading to a holiday camp near Sidmouth. We were going to be there for a few days, so we should have some fun. It was bucketing down as we left Wales. It always seems to rain there. We stopped off at a local baker, as we always did, to buy bundles of Welsh cakes. The old girl behind the counter buttered them up for us and with a jar of Robertson's jam we are in heaven. We went from the rain of Wales to warm sunshine as we headed south.

Holiday camp romps at Sidmouth

I was driving the van near Highbridge, Somerset, when suddenly I heard a loud rattling noise. I stopped on the hard shoulder and got under the van. The exhaust pipe was hanging off. While I was under there I couldn't believe all the holes in the bodywork – it looked like a colander. Des and Gloria somehow got the exhaust back on with tape and some wire. After looking underneath the van I let Des do the driving. I said to him, 'Des, this van is a death trap. This won't see many more miles.'

He replied, scratching his head, 'I must admit there are a few issues with it.'

'This needs to go to the scrapper and quick. Surely with your contacts you can get a better van than this? We've got a few quid in the band's bank account so can we make this a priority.'

We eventually arrived at the holiday camp and laboured up to the gates. Security let us through and the van with Modern Edge stamped all over it got us an enthusiastic welcome from the holidaymakers, especially the girls. I rubbed my hands together and thought, 'Just what the doctor ordered.' We parked the three vehicles next to the theatre. We were greeted by the entertainment manager, a man in his fifties, totally unfazed – he had seen it all before with visiting bands. He showed us where we were playing and pointed to our chalets. We wanted to get on the beach so we set the gear up on stage in record time, dumped our belongings in the chalets and made for the sea. Billy and Gloria stayed in their chalet and went straight on the nest. Des wanted to sort out the van and make a few phone calls, so it was just me and the other three.

With our shorts on and me carrying a football, we were as chuffed as a badger, as they say down this neck of the woods. Once on the beach, it was 'up periscope' time to see where all the girls were. We quickly saw some that looked interesting. We strolled up to them and Steve said with his big mouth, 'Can we join you, girls?'

Their big-mouth replied, 'Looks like you already have.'

We scanned the girls quickly to see who we fancied, then I fell for the oldest trick in the book. Steve kicked the football into the sea. I reckon the fumes in that death trap of a van had got to me as, like a half-wit, I ran into the sea and with difficulty retrieved the ball. When I got back it had all been divvied up. Steve, Rick and Ray were all sitting next to the three best lookers. They were grinning at me like Cheshire cats while I was dripping water everywhere. All that was left was a bird with National Health glasses, dodgy choppers and a bad case of acne, which would be all right for Des. The other one, Ann, wasn't bad but looked frightened of her own shadow. The last one you could see was the first reserve in case one of Steve's, Ray's or Rick's girls blew out. They were from Hull, so there was a language barrier, but once we told them we were the band for the camp's entertainment for the next few days, talking went out the window. While I was trying to chat up Ann, who was a bit quiet, Des turned up looking worried.

'I've got to go back to Romford for a few days,' he said. 'Dad has been arrested on a bank robbery charge.'

Steve says, all cocky like, 'I thought he'd moved on from banks to post offices.'

'Is that meant to be funny?'

'Sorry, Des, only kidding.'

'It can't be him – he's got his account with that bank. He's not going to rob his own bank, is he?' said Des.

Well, we all creased up with laughter. Poor old Des was serious – he really believed that.

Rick said, 'It's a pity you've got to go back – we've lined you up with Dorothy.'

She gave him a smile, showing her mouthful of noshers. Des looked over at her, pulled a face and said under his breath, 'Thank God I'm going back home.'

I took him to one side and said, 'You know me and the boys are there for you. How are you going to get home?'

'I'm going to take the van and while I'm there I'll part-ex it for another one and bring it back before you leave the camp. Don't worry about the money – I'll sort that out. We can worry about the exes later.'

Within half an hour it was like we'd known the girls for ages. We all went into the sea for a swim except Ann, who just had a paddle. She was a likeable girl, about my age, dark wavy hair, with bright blue eyes. I couldn't understand why she was on edge all the time; perhaps it was me, as I can be a bit loud and over the top.

We had to go back to get ready for the gig. We arranged to see them later on at the beach.

The hall was big with a very high ceiling that could cause problems with sound. Fortunately they had a soundman, so that was good news. We met up with him, Josh, a local lad about 25, skinny as a rake with a Beatle haircut and a permanent grin; if you didn't know him you'd think he was fourpence short of a shilling. It was a cabaret setting with a dance floor, seating all round and a large bar at the back – probably held about 500 people. This week we were playing mainly covers as the holidaymakers were from all over the country. Some would never have heard of us, so we'd give them what they knew because after a few sherbets they might get a bit rowdy. We had a good sound check, copied the set lists for everybody and were ready to go. Billy and Gloria were still shagging for Britain as we made our way back to the beach, picking up where we left off.

Ann seemed pleased to see me and told me she worked for the council as a shorthand typist, but there was still that edge with her. The ugly one, the first reserve, who wasn't needed, had gone to pastures new. The boys were slobbing all over their girls and I tried to get a snog with Ann, who moved her head away. There's nothing worse than that when the other three are all over their birds and there's me looking like Billy-no-mates. I might have to find the first reserve as I was not sitting there like a pot plant.

It was time for a game of football on the beach, which the girls joined in. It all got a bit silly after a few minutes as, boys being boys, they started chasing the girls around, which they loved. Then, unintentionally, Rick pulled Ann on to the sand. Ann started crying as, unbeknown to us, including most of her friends, it disturbed a wig she was wearing. The poor girl was as bald as a coot. It didn't help when Steve said, 'Feck me – she's got a syrup on.'

Ann had now run off with the wig in her hand. I chased after her and caught up with her. She was sobbing her heart out. I put my arm around her and gave her a cuddle. After a couple of minutes she calmed down. The girl with Steve knew she had this condition and joined us.

'You all right Ann?'

'Yeah, Julie, it's the embarrassment of it all. I wished the sand could have swallowed me up there and then.'

'Ann, I think you're lovely with or without hair.'

'You're just saying that, Nick, to make me feel better.'

'I'm not. You could be worse, like Steve – plenty of hair but no brains. Hopefully while I'm here we can enjoy some fun together. Is that a date?'

'Yeah, I would like that, Nick.'

'That's great. We've got to go now and get ready for tonight. You will be there?'

'Yeah.'

'Promise?'

'I promise.'

Steve joined us and you could see he was upset at what he'd said to her. 'I'm really sorry, Ann. I shouldn't have said that.'

Julie butted in and said, 'No, you shouldn't. And for that, Steve, there'll be no naughties for you tonight.'

We all laughed. I kissed Ann on the cheek and gave her a quick hug. As I left I looked back and she gave me a wave.

Our sleeping arrangements were well basic. I shared a room with Steve and his stinky feet. In its previous life the room must have been an air-raid shelter. The nosh was fair and, bearing in mind that we weren't paying for it, we couldn't complain. After a large portion of plum duff we went back to the dressing room to get ready. Billy hadn't shown yet, so Ray went to his chalet to kick him out of bed. When Billy did turn up he looked exhausted.

Rick said, 'You're going to have to have a day off from it

otherwise you won't be able to pick up the sticks.'

'Don't you worry about me. You're just envious because you're not getting your fair share at the moment.'

I stepped in, as I could see a bit of aggro starting. 'Save your energy for tonight, you two. Remember this is a three-set night. Which means over three hours playing.'

These nights at holiday camps weren't easy. The owners wanted their pound of flesh from you. Then the punters had their say. What happened was that the first six numbers they listened to you. If they liked you then normally they were OK for the rest of the night. After that you ended up as background music for them while they got the ale down their necks. The problem was that their girlfriends or wives got fed up as no attention was being given to them. They then started to dance together, and started eyeing up the band. Most band members lapped it up, including us. Once the girls had enjoyed a few strong lemonades, between the sets there was a movement outside for a quickie. I knew of a singer called Eric who fronted a band from Southend called Eric C. and the Echoes, who had a quickie one night and didn't come back for the rest of the show and was never seen again. Of course, then what happens is that some of the blokes are missing their birds and go on the hunt for them. It always ends in tears when they see their loved ones in the back of the gig van with some randy musician.

With a long session tonight we'd got ourselves plenty of light ales on stage. There's always an edge when you're about to play. It was a massive old stage as we walked on to play the first number. The hall was packed to the rafters, and the girls from Hull were right in the front ready to dance, all except Ann, which was disappointing. We started off with *Keep On Running* by Spencer Davis, then straight into *Back in the USSR* by the Beatles. We passed the six numbers that we always gauge for the night, all was well, then the real drinking started. We tried not to talk to the crowd a lot, just play. I've been to gigs where the band can't stop talking, the audience gets restless and it all goes downhill. We finished the first set with *Beggin'* by Timebox. As soon as the set finished all the boys jumped off the stage and were among the Hull girls.

I said to Steve's girl, Julie, 'Where's Ann?'

'I'm sorry, Nick, she's still upset about what happened on the beach today.'

I got Ann's chalet number and quickly made my way over there. I knocked on the door and she shouted out, 'Who's there?'

'Only Nick, the big bad wolf.'

She opened the door and gave a weak smile.

'Ann, come and join us. I've only got a few minutes before I'm back on stage.'

'I can't face everybody, Nick, I'm so embarrassed.'

'You're an attractive girl. I don't care about whether you've got hair or no hair. It's you I like as a person. All the guys in the band want you there, as do your friends. So put your gear on and come to the party – it's a great night. I've got to go, so please come.'

'I'll think about it, Nick.'

I gave her a cuddle, kissed her on the cheek and said, 'Ann, I really want you to come.'

As I ran back to the stage I thought to myself, the first reserve is eyeing me up and she ain't bad, just dodgy pins, so why am I messing about with Ann? She really is a nice girl and perhaps I feel sorry for her. But there was something about her that was worth all the effort.

As I entered the hall there was the band just about to start without me. I couldn't believe it. Steve had my Fender and was about to play lead. I jumped on stage and said to him, 'What's happening here?'

'You're late and we can't let the public down I was only going to play lead on the next number.'

'Oh, pull the other one, Steve. You let the public down every time you play bass.'

'What do you mean by that cutting remark?'

'Do you know what your nickname is on the circuit?'

Rick and Ray were both laughing as Billy shouted out, 'Henry Cooper!'

'Where do you get Henry Cooper from?' said a bemused Steve.

Rick, grinning all over his face, shouted, 'Because you play like you've got feckin' boxing gloves on!'

Steve's face was a picture – he was lost for words. He got a strop on and nearly threw the Fender back at me.

When dancing, girls put their handbags in a circle in the middle of the dance area and dance around them. They normally don't like any blokes encroaching on their patch unless they fancy them. Near the end of the second set two lads aged about 15 started acting stupid around the girls. This went on for a few minutes when Julie, Steve's bird, and the first reserve gave them a clump around the ear. They took the hint and quickly left the circle. You didn't mess about with those Hull girls.

We finished the second set and I was pleased that Ann had turned up. I said that as soon as the show finished we'd have a drink. We quickly got into the last set as the band wanted to meet their girls and hopefully go back to their chalets. The last set can be a problem as the punters are now tanked up and are looking for a bird or getting more beer down their throats. I'd never seen a drummer play with his eyes closed, but I did tonight. The four of us couldn't believe what we were seeing. Steve went up to Billy and turned up his bass. That certainly woke him up, when he fell off his stool.

Then it happened, bringing the show to an early end, which suited us. Some blokes from Liverpool and London decided that they wanted to swap chairs! There was an almighty punch-up and we were told to pack up. We were off that stage in seconds. The gear was moved to a safe distance and guitars locked away. We all shot off to another bar with the girls, had a quick drink, then did our own thing. Ann told me she had alopecia, which was why she had total hair loss. It didn't bother me and we had a nice evening together. I stayed with her for the rest of the week, as did the other guys with their girls.

In the daytime Rick, Ray, Steve and I would take the girls out down the coast. Eight-up in a Cortina estate is a bit tight, but great fun. When you're old and decrepit at 40 you can recall the days when you were fancy-free and having a laugh. It was a great week playing and meeting the girls at the holiday camp. When it was time to leave there were lots of tears from the girls, with promises to write and not forget. Then Des eventually did turn up in a

1950s Bedford CA van. We'd gone from a top-dollar custom-built touring bus down to a Transit – now we'd hit rock bottom with another heap of tosh. To be fair, it got us through the Sunshine Tour, which was a great success except for the Anita and Jenny showdown and one or two punch-ups, which was expected.

As we headed home for a few days' break we had lots of things to look forward to. Our new manager, TJ, was good news and I was sure that he'd find us another record company so we'd get that No 1 hit we so desperately wanted.

♫ 7 ♫

The terrible twins

It was great to get home and have a break from touring. We'd been full-on for nearly a year with hardly any time off. I had to grow up pretty quickly when I lost my Mum and Dad, both within a short period of time. All the guys in the band went back to their parents' houses, so it was sad coming back home to an empty house with no Mum and Dad to welcome you. They were great parents and I missed them terribly.

There were some phone calls to make. First I rang Pauline in Great Yarmouth. I wanted to go down and see her as I had some spare time. Unfortunately she was going away on a course so that was the end of that. She was going to ring me when she got back. There had been no more trouble from her ex, which was really good news. I then rang Shelly from the hairdressers to make sure she was all right after what happened in the pub with Anita and Jenny in Reading. She had some surprising news. After the rumpus she had put in her notice to leave the salon. She explained that Anita and Jenny were so shocked at what had happened that night that their attitude towards her and the other members of the salon had changed overnight. It was now a much happier place to work. So some good had come out of that, but that didn't change what Steve and I thought of them both.

Ann from Hull was next on my list. She was really pleased to hear from me and was feeling much more confident in herself. I said I'd meet up with her when we were next playing up North. I felt like Marjorie Proops, the agony aunt, after all the phone calls.

Steve lived down the same street as me and he popped in for a chat. 'We've got all this time off but no ladies in tow,' he said. 'I don't fancy going out looking for it. Any thoughts?'

We both shouted out at the same time, 'The terrible twins, Mandy and Viv!'

We'd known these girls for a few years and they were the female equivalent of us two. They were shockers and didn't hold back. If they liked you, you were well in, if not their tongues were cutting. They were always Mods, sharp dressers with their Twiggy hairstyles. Their parents had stalls down Petticoat Lane in East London selling the latest fashions, mostly off the back of lorries. Mandy's Mum was a right goer and there was a great story about her. She had this bloke in bed and must've worn the poor soul out as he had a heart attack on the job. When the ambulance arrived she said to one of the attendants, 'I didn't know I was that good.'

We hadn't spoken to them for about a year. I rang Mandy up but she was out. Her Mum answered. I knew her and as soon as she knew it was me she suggested she and her mate could meet me and Steve for a drink. I got off that phone like my life depended on it. We didn't want to be ravished by two 40-year-olds who wouldn't take no for an answer at the end of the night.

Steve rang Viv up but she said they both had long-term boyfriends and weren't available, but she'd have a chat with Mandy. That was unusual for them, as they never went out with any blokes for too long. Steve asked who they were going out with and when she told him he couldn't stop laughing. After he put the phone down he said to me, 'Guess who Viv is going out with?'

'Go on, surprise me.'

'Only that dingle, Bruce out of the Dynamos.'

'That dickhead? What about Mandy?'

'Hold on to this – only Dinky!'

'Bleedin' hell, they've dropped their standards.'

I'd better explain who they were. Dinky, who went under the name of Johnny D. Freshman in the music business – real name Donald Spicer – was the singer with our mate Terry and the Tanks. Terry got fed up with him and kicked him out of his group because he was always moaning about something. After that he was nicknamed Dinky because he was always throwing his toys out of the pram. He was a fat little bastard with no personality. Bruce was his best mate, probably his only mate. He was a long streak of piss who thought he could play the guitar and told everybody he was a session musician. He could only play three chords and they were all in H! Dinky started up his own band, Johnny D. Freshman and the Dynamos – what a name to call a band! They were playing in Germany at the moment because nobody would employ them over here – they were crap.

Within a couple of minutes of Steve putting the phone down, Mandy rang back. She was well up for a meet, so we were seeing them Saturday, which was the following day. She made it quite clear that it wasn't just a quick drink and a fumble. They wanted to go out for the day, and Southend was their choice.

We picked them up in Steve's Ford Consul, a nice motor but drank petrol for Shell. He seemed to change his motor every week. Mandy lived in a street in Dagenham that was renowned for being a bit rough. Steve stayed in the motor – he didn't want it to get nicked.

Mandy's Mum answered the door. What a state – Bristols hanging out, dark roots showing through her over-bleached blonde hair, short mini-skirt and bright red lipstick. Other than that she looked fine! Behind her was a carbon copy of her mother. Mandy had a big gob, and as she saw me she shouted, 'Faaackinell, I knew you'd come back for more.'

I quickly threw her in the car as her mate Viv came round the corner with near enough no clothes on. As she got next to the motor this kid of about 13 came round like a maniac on his bike, braked and nearly hit Viv. She did no more than give this kid a clip around the ears, then stamped on his bike as hard as she could. Then she said, spitting out her words, 'You come round here again and I'll box your bleedin' ears in.'

The kid jumped on his bike, which now had a wobbly wheel, and pedalled for all his life. Viv jumped in the front of the motor, gave Steve a snog and said, just like her mate Mandy, 'I'd knew you'd come back for more.'

The terrible twins were a nightmare, but with their hidden talents you had to put up with their rough edges, and there were some. They were in charge today, but hopefully tonight that would all change. As we made our way down the A127 towards Southend, Mandy and Viv wanted to go into the Blinking Owl cafe at Rayleigh for breakfast. This cafe was for Rockers and we,

being Mods, thought it really wasn't a good idea. They won and
Steve pulled into the car park, making sure we kept well away
from the motorbikes. As we were eating our big breakfast a couple
of Rockers on the next table couldn't keep their eyes off the girls.
Mandy had had enough of this and verbally tore into them.

'What you gawking at – haven't you seen a pair of tits before?'
Steve and I cringed behind our sausages, then Viv had her say.
'Yeah, looking at you two, you probably haven't.'
The blokes were lost for words.

We gobbled our breakfast down and quickly shuffled the girls
out of the cafe before we got into any more trouble. We got back
in the motor and made our way to the Kursaal on Southend
seafront. In fact, it was the world's first ever theme park. Steve
put a tape of the Animals on the eight track to drown the girls
squawking. When you think who we had in the motor it was a
good choice of band. Things you have to put up with to hopefully
have some fun later.

I said to Mandy, 'Can we enjoy the rest of the day without you
two getting us into trouble?'

'They kept staring at our breasts – what was I supposed to do?'

'Why don't you cover them up a bit, Mandy?'

'You won't say that tonight, will you, Nick?'

Steve started grinning and said, 'Girls, you've obviously got
class, so what is the attraction of Dinky and his gormless mate
Bruce?'

'Money,' said Mandy.

'You ain't charging now, Mandy?' I said.

'You cheeky bastard! If we were you couldn't afford us, but
it's a thought. My brother collects football pools money around
Rainham and one of his punters had a good win, which he told
us about. The winner was only Dinky's old man. We know Dinky
because of the bands he's played in around here. I made a beeline
for his son and now he thinks he's in love with me. All we're doing
is helping him spend some of his Dad's money, that's all.'

I laughed and said to Viv, 'What about Bruce? You've dropped
your standards there.'

'Dinky and Bruce are joined at the hip, so needs must.'

We hit the Kursaal and thankfully the girls calmed down. We did the lot, bumper cars, the Mont Blanc, aerial flight, water chute and cyclone, to name a few. Afterwards we sat on the sands – sorry, mud – and had our fish and chips, then a walk along the mile-long pier holding hands.

Halfway along the pier Mandy stopped me in my tracks, pulled me towards a seat and said with a soft voice that I'd never ever heard before, 'Nick, we've known each other for a number of years. We always get on well, we have the same chemistry, if you know what I mean.'

What's coming here, I'm thinking to myself. I've never heard it called chemistry before – more like lust. I gently said, 'Well, yeah, we do have a kind of bond.'

'Nick, you've got that house all to yourself. Why don't I come and live with you? I'm sure we can both stop our wandering ways and settle down as a couple. What do you think?'

Bleedin' hell! How was I going to get out of this one? I didn't want to upset her. I'd be knackered after a week of 'chemistry'. I chose my words carefully and said, as lovingly as possible, 'Mandy, I don't know what to say. I'm very fond of you and the idea seems very appealing, but there is one problem.'

'What's that then, Nick?'

'I think you know I have a brother, Arthur, who at the moment lives in Canada. Unfortunately, he's coming back very soon to live with me so I won't be on my own.'

'Oh.'

'But I'll tell you what. Why don't you stay with me for a few days and have a dry run to see how we get on.'

She brightened up immediately and said, 'I'm all for that, Nick.'

I have to say that the two days with her were great. She cooked nice meals, did the dusting, was a wizard with the hoover and the 'chemistry' was full on at any time of the day. She did show her true colours once with the poor old milkman. Because of the birds pecking the top of the milk, I had a box outside so he could put the milk in there. Unfortunately for him he forgot to do it one day and the birds pecked the cream off the gold top. As the milkman walked away, Mandy opened the door and shouted at him, 'Milky, are you thick or something?'

'Sorry, madam – have you a problem?'

'Because you never put the bottles in the box yesterday the tits pecked at my gold top.'

The bloke didn't know where to put his face. I knew what he was thinking and what he would have liked to have said. He smirked and said, 'I'm sorry about that, madam.'

'Don't smirk at me! I'm not your normal customer, you dongle. I want both bottles replaced free of charge. And for my inconvenience I also want two large bottles of orange, otherwise there'll be a short in your electric cart when I put a screwdriver through the fuse box.'

'I don't think I can do that.'

'Do you want to face me every morning?'

He thought about it for a moment and quickly went and got the milk and orange from his cart. Mandy slammed the door and said, 'That's how to deal with them milkies. How many eggs do you want for your breakfast, Nick?'

'Two, please. And a glass of orange would be nice.'

I said goodbye to Mandy the next day and I have to say that it was a scream living with her – we did have a laugh. Unfortunately the laughs finished when the phone rang.

♫ 8 ♫

Big Al to the rescue

I picked up the phone and it was TJ. After a 10-minute conversation it was bad news. The band was going to have a big cash flow problem that could jeopardise our existence and the dream of a No 1 hit. I got in touch with the guys, including Des, and we had a band meet that night at our local, the Queen's Arms.

We got the Double Diamond in, lit up some of Des's Rothmans kingsize and I explained what our problem was.

'TJ belled me this morning. The bad news is that he can't sign us up for another four months.'

'Hang about!' said Ray. 'We're signing the contract next Wednesday. Our gigs run out in a month's time. He had all the new one's lined up.'

'That means no gigs for three months, which means no money,' said Rick.

'What's brought all this on then, Nick?' said Steve.

'That divvy Julian has read the real small print in the contract and because TJ was with them for over five years he can't start up a similar agency for six months. He's taken legal advice and they confirm the company are in their rights to do this. We'll still sign the contract next week, but it won't start until a six-month period has expired.'

'How can he do that if he is black-balled?' piped up Billy.

'His brother is fronting the new business in his name. It will transfer over to TJ when everything is finalised.'

'We've had this before with a previous record company in '67,' said Steve. 'What was that bloke's name...?'

'Johnny Curtis,' I said. 'He held our new record company to ransom. They didn't want to record us again but wouldn't release us from our contract, which still had a few months to go.'

'That's it,' said Des. 'Your old man got involved, didn't he,

Rick? He got some of the chaps to pay him a visit and, Bob's your uncle, Johnny Curtis decided overnight it would be in his interest to release us immediately.'

'I'm not getting my Dad involved again. He's already visited Chelmsford and Wormwood Scrubs – my Mum would go ape shit if he got involved with anything iffy again.'

'Look, the bottom line is that we need a few gigs to tide us over before we join TJ. I've got one or two ideas, so leave it to me. Plus it will give us an opportunity to learn some new numbers and, more importantly, some of our new material, which we'll need to take to the record company. You never know, one of them could be that No 1 hit we all dream about.'

'Dream on, Nick. I've got HP payments on my keyboard to keep up. I can't mess about with lots of rehearsing. I need gigs.'

'Rick, we've all got HP payments – you're no different to any of us.'

I looked over to Des, who was deep in thought. I wondered whether he might get Monty involved to change Julian's mind. Des was so loyal to the band and with his circle of associates it was best not to think about it. I did worry that we seemed to be shifting nearer to those people whenever we needed some help.

We met TJ and signed the contract. Steve's Dad, Tom, was with us and he was happy everything was in order. He was sorry that we'd got to hang about longer than anticipated. He told us about the gigs he'd got lined up for us, and they were top dollar. We were going to get more money for those gigs as well, which was good news.

I started to try and find some work to keep us going. First call was to Big Al. He was my age and king of the Rockers in Hornchurch and Upminster. I'd known him since I was 11, when we played in the Hornchurch district football team. He played for an Upminster school and I played for Ardleigh Green junior school. We used to play against Barking, Dagenham and West Ham schools, where a lot of the players went on to play professional football with West Ham, Tottenham, Leyton Orient and Arsenal. I'd had a couple of games for Ipswich youth team.

I'd lost contact with him until a few years back. It was funny how we met up again. Back in 1964 Steve and I went down to Brighton in my black Ford 100E, the year when the Mods and Rockers were kicking off. On the way there a fight broke out on the roadway. We stopped and, while they were kicking the crap out of each other, two Mod girls, who were there with their boyfriends, were looking on, and weren't impressed. We offered them a lift to Brighton, and in fact Maureen and Wendy stayed with us for the weekend. We stopped off at a cafe, and as we came out their boyfriends and their mates were on their Vespas and Lambrettas. As soon as they saw us we were set upon and in for a hiding. In the distance the roar of motorbikes put a stop to that. We were in a no-win situation as we were Mods. The dozen or so Rockers came up to us and it looked like bother. The main man came forward and I recognised him immediately – it was Big Al. He soon sorted the Mods out, then gave me his telephone number. I made contact with him when we got back and he joined us as a roadie for one of our tours in the South West.

I hadn't spoken to him for about a year. The last time I heard he was promoting bands at local dance halls and coffee bar gigs we used to do before we became more main-line.

Big Al was pleased to hear from me and we had a meet at the White Hart pub in Hornchurch. His long hair was even longer, he was unshaven and, at six feet plus, he looked intimidating. Once we got all the current news out of the way I asked if he could get us any gigs on his circuit. He was gobsmacked that we wanted to go back to much smaller venues, for probably a quarter of the money that we were getting now. I explained the situation, and he was more than happy to take us on board for a few gigs, bearing in mind that we were a national band, although most of us came from the area. Except for the money, it wouldn't do us any harm to go back to our roots and play some small and intimate venues again.

As Al explained, 'You're lucky, Nick, because I'm just about to book my last bands for the next two months, then I'm off to Australia.'

'Christ, mate, who's after you?'

'There's some up-and-coming bands over there and I want to get involved in managing some of them. Also, I have one or two issues here that are best resolved from a distance.'

'Where's Sampson?'

'Unfortunately he died a few weeks back. I really miss him. As I'm moving to Oz I haven't got another dog.'

Big Al had always had a big dog ever since I'd known him, and he always calls them Sampson. A few times, when promoters wouldn't pay, Big Al and his dog would pay them a visit and, funnily enough, they paid straight away!

Al then said something that made me feel uneasy. 'Des still works for you doesn't he?'

'Yeah, why?'

'Well, I know he thinks the world of your band and would do anything for you. As you know he does mix with, let's say, some shady characters. I think he is getting more involved with some of the chaps than he should do, that's all.'

'Yeah, point taken.'

'It's just a word of caution, that's all, Nick. You don't want your band to get involved.'

I changed the subject quickly and said, 'We've got a month's work, so after that anything you can do for us for that last month before you go away, I'd be grateful.'

'Take it as a done deal. You being a main-liner, it will fill the dance halls and I'm going to find out if I can get the theatre in Romford for my last gig, which will be my swansong.'

♫ 9 ♫

The Windmill where it all began

Big Al came good and got us a few bookings, plus an empty slot at the two-tier theatre at Romford. If we filled it we'd earn well out of it. The dance halls he'd got for us in Essex were where we first started out, like the Windmill in Upminster, and Wykeham Hall in Romford where, if you went out and came back in the hall, they stamped your hand so they knew you'd paid. Also the Masonic, All Saints and North Street halls, all in Hornchurch. Now, it might sound naff that some of these halls were church youth clubs. Youngsters flocked to these venues for live music. Bands would cut their teeth in places like this and many a band went on to make records. And if you got 150 teenagers in a small hall, dancing and enjoying themselves, you couldn't help but pull. Once you'd met the girls, word spread about parties. It was great being a teenager in the '60s and '70s.

Al lined us up with a couple of coffee bars, the La Saucier in Hornchurch and the Sombrero. Except for the money, I was looking forward to playing these again. All these places were within 10 miles of where we lived, so there were no overnight stays and we saved a lot of money on fuel.

We completed the last of the bookings for that snake Julian. We'd been with the company for a number of years under the management of TJ. If he'd still been there I couldn't have seen us leaving, but life moves on and we were looking forward to working with him again soon. We had a few days before our first booking with Big Al at the Windmill on Friday night.

Pauline from Yarmouth made contact with me and it was bad news. Her Dad, whom she idolised, had died. She was in the process of sorting out his affairs, then wanted to move to London. I gave her TJ's phone number as she had mentioned to me before that she wanted to get into the music business. I told her to mention my name – hopefully that wouldn't put him off!

After Al's bookings we had no more gigs lined up, which meant a month of no money – not good news. On the Thursday before the gig at the Windmill I was in Monty's cafe with Steve and Des, and the breakfast was swimming in more fat than usual. I said to Steve, 'Have a word with Monty about changing this breakfast. There's more fat on here than on your last bird, Steve.'

'You're taking the piss.'

'No.'

'If you think I'm going to tell Monty, you've got another think coming. I like living.'

Suddenly Monty appeared from the back of the cafe and called me. I hoped he hadn't heard what I'd just said.

'Nick, there's a phone call for you. Hurry up about it, as I'm waiting for an urgent business call.'

I came back a few minutes later and told the lads what the call was about. As I did so I looked at Des.

'You won't believe this! That was TJ – he's been trying to get hold of me all morning. Ray told him where I'd probably be. One of the blokes he worked with at his previous company has told him that they've had a small fire in one of their offices. All the contracts for artistes and former employees, including his one, have gone up in smoke.'

I looked again at Des, but there wasn't a flicker of emotion.

'What does that mean to us?' asked Steve.

'Well, he's said that if the contract has been destroyed then he's going full throttle with his business. How can they take him to court without a contract? So within a month we'll be with him and all our problems are solved. Just Big Al's gigs to do and we're back on the road again.'

'How did the fire start? Well handy for us, and of course him,' Steve said.

'They reckon it was started by an electrical fault.'

As I said this Des coughed and sputtered over the tea he was drinking. Steve and I looked at him – we both knew what we were thinking. Nothing more was said and it wasn't mentioned again.

As we were making our way home, I said to Steve, 'Bit of a coincidence about that fire. What do you think?'

'Let's be honest – there's more chance of West Ham winning three matches in a row than that fire being an accident.'

We were really looking forward to our first gig under Big Al. The Windmill dance hall in Upminster looked like a long air-raid shelter. There was a small stage and the hall took about 100-plus people. Before we played there we used to come with our mates, dance a good twist and chat up plenty of girls. There was no alcohol allowed and we rarely saw any drugs – we didn't need stimulants to arouse our hormones. The atmosphere of crowds of us dancing to the loud pulsating music of the Rolling Stones' *Paint It Black* through a haze of Woodbine smoke or, if you were rich, Senior Service, was enough to get any bloke's sap rising. I remember when we played here before in 1965. It was a great night, and even better when they installed some new lighting above the dance floor. They switched the lights on and we couldn't believe our eyes – this lighting was so strong it shone through the girls' skirts! It showed all their underwear. Some of the girls had no underwear on, and ran off the dance floor in all directions screaming – it was handsome!

Friday was always a terrific night there. It was for 15-to-18-year-olds, mostly Mods and a few Mockers who couldn't make up their mind whether they were a Mod or a Rocker. Living near London, when teenagers left school at 15 a lot of them went to work mostly in the City and the West End. The girls worked as shorthand typists, punch-card operators and shop assistants at some of the well-known stores in Regent Street and Oxford Street. The blokes also worked in the City as messenger boys or clerks at stockbrokers, shipping lines and banks. They all had one thing in common. Working in London, most of them wore the up-to-date fashions: the girls with their Mary Quant mini-skirts, hot pants, paisley print mini-dresses, or tie-dyed shirts with bell-bottom jeans and go-go boots. Hairstyles went from beehives, bouffant or a page boy flip. The guys had their Harrington jackets, button-down Fred Perry shirts and winkle-pickers so pointed you could burst a balloon with the point.

We got there early and met up with Big Al. We set up the amps, drums and the rest of the gear. We were having a problem with Billy. His bird Gloria had gone back home to live, as her Dad was now hoping to retire early and he wanted her to run the garage business. Knowing her, she was well capable. Billy was lovesick and she was missing him. That doesn't mix in bands, and I could see him moving up to Suffolk and jacking the band in.

With an hour to go, a lot of the young people were over at the Sombrero coffee bar having their frothy coffees. We were all set and really up for it, especially when Diane walked in looking really tasty, and she brought a few of our old friends with her. Touring as we did, we didn't see enough of them. I made a beeline for Diane, but gently, as she knew me of old. Her brother, Pete, had helped us get started in the music business. He had worked for one of the music papers and had been a great help to us. Diane was my age. She had these eyes, slightly slanted, Chinese-looking. She had dark short hair in a bob and there was a twinkle in her eyes when she smiled. She was well savvy and knew every trick in the book when a bloke was trying to chat her up. I went straight over to her and tried my luck.

'Great to see you here tonight. No boyfriend?'

'You've heard then that we've split up.'

Now, me being very considerate and understanding, I went straight in with, 'Sorry to hear that.'

'No you're not, Nick – you think you've got a chance now.'

'Well, as it happens that did cross my mind.'

As she walked away she said with a grin, 'You never know…'

I couldn't wait for the gig to finish. Des brought his latest girl, Alice, and she certainly wasn't in Wonderland! Unfortunately, the girl looked like a hamster in a dress. Steve went straight in at Des and said, 'What hutch did you get her out of?'

'I wouldn't take the mick if I was you, Steve. That girl you're with was in the local newspaper a while back.'

'What're you on about?'

'Do you remember the girl who got kidnapped by her boyfriend because she wanted to pack him up?'

'Yeah, I remember – he was a right nutter.'

'The bird you're with is that girl.'

'You're winding me up, Des!'

'Even Monty's lot keep away from him. When he comes out of

prison, as far as he is concerned she's his property.'

We had to get Steve a glass of water before he fainted.

We did the last checks on the little stage, plugged in the Vox amps and Billy adjusted his drums. We did the 1-2-3 on the mics and we were ready to go. The hall was crammed wall to wall and everybody was out for a good time. It's a silly thought that tonight there'd be blokes chatting up girls they didn't know and one of them might end up marrying them. My mate Mick and I came here a few years back and he met a girl, did a bit of courting, got engaged and married her. He'd dropped a right bollock – his mother-in-law was a nightmare and her Dad was the copper that had nicked him for tea-leafing some lead flashing off a church roof – the church they attended every week.

I looked at the lads before we opened up with *Shakin' All Over* by Johnny Kidd and the Pirates. There's nothing better than playing music with your mates. I loved that number as I could really express myself on lead, and I was up for it. Within 10 minutes the hall was rocking and we were taking the roof off. Sweat was pouring off me as riffs come fast and furious. Everybody was dancing and Ray's strong and powerful voice was echoing around the hall. Rick was on top form on keyboards – he wanted to impress his new bird, who'd gone all gooey-eyed. Poor old Steve has gone into Henry Cooper mode with his bass playing. The thought of a psychopath rotting in prison pining for the bird that he was going out with didn't bear thinking about. Billy was knocking crap out of his drums as usual, so no change there. We played the numbers one after another without any chat in between till the end of the first set.

During the break we downed some light ales that we'd brought with us. Big Al came over – he was well happy with us.

Diane was hovering nearby and I shot over there like a ferret down a drain pipe. Without being flash, I said, 'Did you enjoy the music?'

'It was all right, but I've heard better from Dinky's band, John D. Freshman and the Dynamos.'

Christ, this is going to be hard work, I thought. That was the best I'd played for a long time, plus the extra Old Spice and

clean pants. I got a bit sarky and said to her, 'Dinky's band? You're
having a bleedin' laugh!'

'No I'm not – they're playing at The Shed over at Harold Hill
next week. All the girls are going.'

I walked off with a right cob on and went outside for a gasper.
As I made my way back to the stage, Diane came up to me and
said, 'Nick, I was only joking. Steve told me to say all that.'

I looked over to the stage and he had this silly grin all over his
face. I shouted out, 'I wouldn't laugh, Steve. Des has just seen your
bird's kidnapper walk in.'

'I thought the band played really well, Nick, you especially,' she
said.

'Can I walk you home after the gig, Diane?'

'I'd love that, Nick.'

After that, I was smitten. The second set was just as good as the
first. I don't think I'd enjoyed a gig as much for a long time. Times
like that will stay in my mind all my life. It might sound stupid,
but there'll be a time when I'm chatting to the lads in the care
home and we can reminisce about the old days!

After the gig Al paid us in pound notes, which was handy. It
was a profitable night for him, so he bunged us a few quid extra.

I took Diane home and we stayed together for a couple of
weeks before she flew off to see her brother in America. TJ got in
touch – the fire had certainly brought things forward. As soon as
we'd finished Al's last gig at the theatre in Romford, we were on
board with TJ. He was a diamond – he said he should have enough
work to take us well into the end of 1970. There was more good
news when Pauline rang from Yarmouth. She had an interview
fixed with TJ. I rang him after to say she was well worth taking on
board. He wanted a booker for his bands, so it was an important
job.

We had a spare night, so Steve, Terry from the Tanks and
myself went down to see Dinky's band play at The Shed, which
was in the middle of a rough council estate. It was a desperate
place and you had to be struggling to want to play there. Terry told
us they had got booted out of Germany and were taking anything
on offer at the moment.

'I thought his old man won the pools. Surely he's bunged him a few bob,' I said..

'You're joking! His old man hates him.'

'Poor old Dinky – at least Mandy likes him,' Steve said, laughing.

'As soon as Mandy knows there's no dough coming her way she'll knock him into touch,' I said.

There were about 100 people in the dive. There was a pub up the road called the Pompadours, nicknamed the 'Flying Bottle', and quite a few would have a few pints before they came in. If they didn't like you they soon made it clear by throwing you and your gear off the stage. Dinky and his rabble were just finishing setting up as we made our way over to them to take the mick.

Terry was straight in with, 'That was a short visit to Germany, Dinky!'

'It's not Dinky, it's Johnny, and we came back early because our management team had arranged a tour for us across Northern Ireland.'

Steve looked at him like he was on drugs, and said, 'There's a feckin' war over there, Dinky. Nobody goes over there.'

Dinky looked over at his band and said to them, cocky like, 'That doesn't worry us, boys, does it?'

His lead guitarist, Bruce, wobbled over to us. He looked like he'd had a handful of purple hearts and, with a spliff hanging out of his mouth, he said, 'No, Johnny, we're not worried. It'll be peace not war when they hear my guitar playing.'

I couldn't help myself when I hit back with, 'Have you mastered Bert Weedon's book *Learning how to play the Guitar* yet?'

Suddenly Steve shouted out, 'The terrible twins are here – hold on to your dicks!'

Mandy and Viv made an entrance with the shortest mini-skirts I'd ever seen. They came straight over and Mandy gave me a snog, much to the annoyance of Dinky, who said, 'That's my bird you're snogging.'

Mandy took me to one side and said, 'Dinky is getting the last rites later, so make sure your front door's open tonight.'

♫ 10 ♫

New management and new drummer

It seemed that the last few months it'd been more about girls than playing. If we wanted to be a serious contender as a main-line band and get that top place in the charts, the serious work needed to start now.

We did the last gig for Big Al at Romford and wished him well for his trip to Aussie. We were now in the hands of TJ. Steve's Dad, Tom, had a long chat with him to make sure everything was correct. He was happy we weren't getting stitched up. We'd written some new material and played it to him. He liked what he heard and was actively looking for a new record deal for us. He'd signed up other bands and one or two of them were top notch, so he meant business. His office wasn't cheapskate, and even though we got on well with him we knew we were only as good as our last gig. If we didn't pull the punters in we were under no illusion, we'd be on our bike. While the band, including Des, was in the office sorting out last-minute details, who should walk in but Pauline from Yarmouth.

TJ said, 'Nick, I think you know Pauline. I've just taken her on today. She's one of my new bookers – she'll be looking after your band and of course a few other bands in the stable.'

Ray said sarcastically, 'What are we now – feckin' racehorses?'

Pauline looked awkward as TJ said, 'Mind the language, Ray – only thoroughbreds, not donkeys, on this circuit.'

We all looked at him. How he'd changed. He now had that hard look about him that you get when you run your own business. I was having doubts about whether it was all going to work out with him. He looked at Des and was quite cutting when he said, 'The last couple of gig vans you got were crap. You need to get a decent one. I can't afford you lot breaking down every other day.'

'You paying for it, then?' said Steve.

'Look, don't get clever. I don't get involved with that – that's your problem. It's all in the contract if you read it.'

The way he was talking it was like we were pieces of meat. We were all getting well annoyed. We concluded our business with him and went over to Lyons Corner House for coffee. Pauline came with us as TJ wanted her to have a chat with us. Billy got the coffees in and Rick said to her abruptly, 'You're our new boss then?'

Pauline looked embarrassed. 'I wouldn't put it like that. I just liaise with you and organise the gigs and hopefully we work as a team.'

Ray, who wasn't impressed, said, 'But you haven't done this before.'

'No, I haven't, so it's a learning curve for me.'

'So you're going to learn on us?' said Steve.

Pauline started to get off her bike and snapped back, 'Look, that's how it is – take it or leave it.'

She got up from her chair, gulped her coffee down and walked out. I followed her and said, 'You never told me you'd got the job.'

'Look, Nick, it all moved very fast. I should've rung you – sorry about that.'

'Where are you living now?'

'TJ found me a flat in Ilford.'

Sarcastically, I responded, 'It looks like he's going to be a nice boss – maybe too nice.'

'What do you mean by that, Nick?'

'Nothing. Ilford's not far from me – it would be great to see each other on a more regular basis.'

'Look, Nick, he wants me to distance myself from any personal involvement with clients. It has got to be on a strictly business level.'

I looked at her and couldn't believe what she'd just said. 'So you're saying that we can't see each other and I'm now called a client not a friend to go out with?'

'You know what I mean, Nick.'

'No, I don't. I think you're well out of order and getting above your station. This is Nick who had your ex sorted out because he was stalking and threatening you.'

'You did that?'

'Well, of course. Do you think there was a fairy godmother that said abracadabra and he disappeared from the scene? Get real, Pauline – I cared about you and I didn't want to see you get hurt, so steps were taken to protect you, which fortunately worked. And another thing – I put a good word in for you with TJ about you getting the job. With the upset you've had in your life recently it was the least I could do for you.'

'I don't know what to say, Nick.'

'Best not to say anything. Enjoy your new job. You'll be talking to Steve's Dad, Tom, about our bookings, not us.'

I was well upset when I went back to tell the lads what happened. There wasn't any sympathy there, as Steve laughingly said, 'You seem to be having a problem with your love life. Anita and Pauline have both knocked you into touch, and Diane has left the country.'

'Mind you, you've always got Mandy – she loves you,' laughed Rick.

'It gets worse – her Mum keeps phoning me up. I've got to get away from them – I'm knackered. The problem is I can't say no to Mandy.'

'Well, we're off to Scotland next week, so it'll give you something else to worry about,' said Rick.

'What do you mean?'

'Remember the last time we played Scotland, we got a right barracking, they hated us.'

On the upside, Steve and I got a nice royalty cheque for *Suburban Mod*, and both agreed that the money would go towards getting another gig van. I went and saw Tom on behalf of the band to make sure he could still look after some of our affairs. He was as sweet as a nut and had no problem helping us out. Steve was lucky to have a Dad like that, who was as good as gold, as was his Mum. There was only one fault with her – she would still buy Camp coffee, like my Mum used to do. I hated the stuff.

We had a bit of luck with another van. Des and I bumped into my old boss, Eddie Tucker, in Monty's cafe. When I left school at 15 I went and worked for him as a second-hand car salesman, more like a general dogsbody. Eddie was a typical car dealer, in his thirties, swarthy, shifty, tinted glasses, gold medallions and a crombie.

He greeted me with his loud cockney accent, 'Hello, my son – still making people go deaf?'

'Tucked anybody up lately, Eddie?'

'Nick, would I do that?'

'Oh, leave it out – what about that poor vicar who bought the Austin A40 from you and asked you what guarantee he got with it? You turned around to him and said it was guaranteed to get you off the forecourt, Vic.'

'What do you expect for a hundred notes?'

'He'd only gone up the road a few yards and half the wing fell off with crud. To make it worse, you'd filled it in with *Tit-Bits* magazines and Polyfilla – the mags were hanging out the hole. His eyes were like pissholes in snow when he saw them naughty ladies.'

'Those days are finished – I'm now legit. I've got a nice showroom off the Romford Road near the dog track. You won't believe it, but I'm dealing with the local constabulary now.'

The cafe went quiet, and the no-neck brigade gave him the evil look. Eddie backtracked quickly. 'I buy their vehicles when they've finished with them.'

The no-neck brigade went back to planning their next jobs.

'It's a pity you're a crook, Eddie, otherwise I'd ask you if you've got any vans for sale.'

'As it happens, I've got just what you want. Come down tomorrow and I'll show you. And by the way, you saucy git, who gave you that Commer van for nothing when you first started out with the band?'

'I have to say, Eddie, that van was a good 'un.'

'See, I did look after you.'

'You held that one back with the rest of the decent motors.'

'What do you mean, held it back?'

'Well, if you remember, the night before, which was Bonfire Night, we were at the Queen's Arms having a drink when you got a phone call at the pub to say your car lot was on fire. You got the drinks in and later one of your mates turned up with singed eyebrows and no hair. It was funny how all the old bangers went up in smoke but the real McCoy motors somehow escaped the fire. Funny that, Eddie…'

Next day Des and I turned up at Tucker's Smart Autos. It didn't look like Eddie had gone up-market with his motors – they still looked like heaps of crap. Eddie came out of the Portakabin looking more dodgy than normal.

'Hello, lads, it's round the back. Don't want people to think I'm in league with the Old Bill.'

'What're you talking about, Eddie?'

'Here it is, low mileage, service history, four new tyres and one careful owner.'

'Where is it then?' said a bemused Des.

'Over here – look.'

'But the only thing that's here is that Austin Black Maria. I've been in a few of them,' said Des, laughing.

'That's it – your new group van.'

'You're having a laugh, Eddie!'

'Come and have a look around it before you pooh-pooh it.'

Reluctantly we looked. He opened the back up and there was oodles of room.

'I have to say it's in good nick.'

'Is that meant to be a bad joke, Des?' I said.

Eddie now went in for the kill as he went into his patter. 'Look at the benefits. Nobody is going to try and break in and nick your gear when you're touring with a blue light on top. Park anywhere. It's been well looked after so it won't let you down, and the bonus is that I'll let you have it for a song. Can I stick you down for it, lads?'

Before we bought it, Des checked it out; he knew everything about motors. We also made sure that Eddie really owned it – I knew him from old. It all stacked up and we made sure the other lads were happy. They thought, like us, that it'd be a bit of a laugh travelling around the country in it.

Before we went to Scotland for ten days we popped into

Monty's for a greasy. It was well busy in there as Monty was having a crime meeting with his local Mafioso. As we were having our nosh, Tommy, one of the regulars, came into the cafe in a blind panic.

'There's a Black Maria outside! Hide everything and keep your heads down. Old Bill is on the target.'

We all started laughing, and he wasn't happy when he was told it was our new group bus. Suddenly Monty left his cronies and came and sat at our table, something he never did. Now, Des had been acting strange for a couple of weeks like he wanted to tell us something.

'Have you told them yet, Des?'

'No, Monty, funnily enough I was just about to give them the good news.'

'Let me tell them.'

Quick as a flash Des jumped in and said, 'No, it's OK, Monty, I'll do it.'

'Good boy. I'll get Rose to bring over six more teas for you.'

As he left there were ten eyes looking at Des, who looked right sheepish. Ray, smelling a rat, fronted up Des and said, 'What's the good news, then, Des? Had it off on the pools?'

Looking awkward as he gulped his tea down, Des muttered, 'Well, the good news is that Monty has asked us to play at a celebration party for one of the chaps at a top West End club.'

'Well, what's the good news, then, Des?' says Billy with a smirk on his face.

I butted in. 'Des, our contract clearly states we can't do any foreigners while we're under TJ's management.'

'Do you want to tell Monty you're refusing his request?'

I looked over at Monty and his henchmen who were eyeballing us, and just shook my head.

Monty then shouted over to us, 'I'll let you know the details soon, boys.'

The Scottish gigs were a nightmare. It started off well as we shot up the A1 in the Black Maria. Des wore a chauffeur's uniform – he looked like a copper. There was enough room for the gear and all of us to travel in style. We looked like criminals as we looked

out of the slit windows. All the fun stopped when we hit Scotch
Corner. The weather closed in and it was blizzard conditions all
the way to Jockland. After that it was downhill all the way. Cold,
wet, snow, wind, half-empty halls and food poisoning. The girls
all seemed to have ginger hair and freckles and the welcomes were
as cold as an Eskimo's todger. When we finished our last gig in
Dundee we legged it straight home.

As soon as I got home I got a phone call from TJ. He wasn't a
happy bunny. 'Didn't go well in Scotland, then, Nick?'

I was getting tired of him treating us like schoolboys. 'No, as it
happens it didn't. We played as well as we could with frostbite in
our fingers.'

'You'll need to do better when you go and do that tour of
universities and colleges soon.'

I completely lost it through lack of sleep, frustration and him
talking to me like I was a dickhead.

'Don't treat me like a schoolboy and you're the headmaster!
Who the bleedin' hell do you think you are? You don't pay me
enough for me to listen to all this shit.'

'Calm down, Nick – we'll speak tomorrow. Pauline will phone
you later to go over the details for next week.'

'I don't want to speak to her – let her go through Tom. She's
another one who's on my hate list.'

I slammed the phone down and went to bed. A few hours later
Steve rang and said he was coming round as there was a major
problem. I was still in my 'Thunderbirds' dressing gown when
Steve came in. I hunted around for some coffee, but all I could find
was my old Mum's bleedin' Camp, which had been there since the
year dot. I sat there wrapping my hands around the cup. I was still
cold from that Godforsaken place called Scotland.

I said, 'So what's going down, Steve?'

'Billy has jacked the band in.'

'I'm surprised there aren't more casualties after the
Armageddon trip. At least we can take our ear plugs out now.'

'Bleedin' hell, Nick, you're giving me the ache. Have another
mouthful of Camp and listen. Oh, by the way, we're seeing the
terrible twins tonight I think we both need a livener.'

'Yeah, I could do with some more humpty dumpty. Sorry about being neg – I'm all ears. I can see we've got a problem. Why's he called it a day, or can I guess?'

'He's missing his bird Gloria and he's fed up of travelling all over the country and earning peanuts.'

'I'm afraid that's the name of the game,' I said.

'He's moving to Suffolk as she's now running her Dad's business full time and the little snake has already got himself another band that gigs around East Anglia so he can get home every night.'

'He has been a busy boy. He could've kept us in the frame about his intentions. I think his prick is ruling his brain. On that subject, what time are we seeing Mandy and Viv?'

We both burst out laughing as Steve said, 'I have to say, Nick, you're taking this very calmly, bearing in mind he's going to leave us in a week and that means no drummer.'

'We've got a drummer.'

'What do you mean?'

'Look, I knew this was going to happen sooner rather than later, so when TJ told us about seeing Tony in a group in Kent I contacted him. Cut a long story short, he'd love to come back and play with us. If you, Rick and Ray agree and he gives us assurances that he's off the drugs, he's on board. I've already squared it off with TJ in case it happened, so he's happy as long as, like us, he isn't popping pills for Essex.'

Tony joined us straight away and we bid Billy farewell. As mentioned before, he was the leader of the band when we first started in 1964 and he was a first-class stick man. We had a few days off so we rehearsed with Tone to bring him up to speed with our numbers. It was like he'd never been away. It was very emotional working with him again. Tone had lost weight and his 6-foot-plus frame looked like he could do with beefing up – plenty of fry-ups on the road would sort that out. He still had his long dark hair dangling to his shoulders and droopy moustache, and he was now sporting an earring. He looked more like a hippy than a clean-cut '60s boy like us! We stopped for a break.

He still had that devil in him when he said, 'It's great to be back. And by the way – Penny and baby Robin send their love.'

I've never seen four blokes go so white at the same time. The conversation went dead. Earlier I mentioned that more than likely one of the band members was the father when she toured with us as our drummer. Steve stuttered out his words when he said to Tone, 'Has baby Robin got a middle name?'

'Funnily enough, he's got more than one. His full name is Robin Rick Billy Steve Nick Ray Des Minster.'

Just at that moment Des entered the church hall where we were practising. All eyes were focused on him. He looked uncomfortable and said, 'What's wrong, lads?'

The thought never went through our minds that he could've dipped his wick with Penny.

On seeing Tone, Des went over and embraced him. They were once great mates, and Des said to him, 'Great to have you back on board again, Tone,' then added, 'We need to talk lads. I'll make the tea first.'

Des brought in the teas from the kitchen and nicked some Penguins out of a biscuit barrel that the vicar had.

'So what's all this about, Des?' I asked.

He took a deep breath and a slurp of tea, then said, 'Remember when we were in Monty's cafe and he talked about a celebration party. It's next Wednesday. I've checked the gig list and we have a spare night, thank goodness.'

Rick smelt a rat and fronted up Des. 'Look, do I look like I've got a carrot on my head. Why do we owe Monty?'

Des looked at me for support and I spoke out for him. 'Rick, look, we didn't want to get other people involved.'

'Well go on then. Am I the last person to know what's happening in the band?'

'No, Rick, I'll explain. When I met Pauline in Yarmouth she had a boyfriend. She jacked him in and as you know I went out with her. He became a pest, so much so that he was stalking and threatening her.'

'So what's that got to do with the band and Monty?' asked an annoyed Rick.

'Well, we all know that Ray was on an ABH charge and that threatened the band.'

'You've lost me.'

Des cut across me and said, 'Look, Monty's boys duffed up the bloke who was putting the bubble in on Ray with the police. Ray would've gone to prison if he'd been found guilty. We couldn't allow that.'

Ray looked at Rick and said, 'We wanted to keep you and the others out of the problem in case it went bandy and he complained to the police about being leant on.'

I continued the story. 'While Monty's boys were up in Norfolk they paid Pauline's ex a visit, and he's now off her radar.'

Rick looked really shocked when he said, 'I'm glad I didn't know any of this. I had all this with my old man and look what happened to him – three years in Chelmsford Prison.'

'That's why we owe Monty for these two problems he solved,' I said.

Des spluttered and starting coughing, finally getting his words out. 'Well, er, it's like this. I asked another favour. So in fact it's three. Well, it did allow you to get on the road much quicker with TJ.'

We looked at him in amazement and just shook our heads in disbelief. Tony, who'd been listening to all this, said, 'What have I got myself involved with?'

♫ 11 ♫

The piper calls the tune

None of us wanted to play this gig for Monty. Our contract with TJ clearly stated that we couldn't do any other work for anybody else, otherwise he could cancel our contract. How we got into all this mess still amazes me. All we wanted to do was play music, but trouble seemed to follow us. The worry was that Des was a bigger player with Monty's firm than we had first thought, otherwise Monty wouldn't have put himself at risk for him.

The venue was a nightclub in the middle of the West End. Sammy, Monty's son, was giving out the orders and you didn't argue with him. He wanted all of us to wear the same suits for the gig and sent us down to Brent & Collins in Romford to get them off the peg. He bunged us a few quid, which just about covered the cost. It all seemed cloak and dagger stuff to me. We really didn't know who we were playing for – it could be a 21st birthday, engagement or anniversary. But it must have been important for them to shell out for new suits for us, which were a nice light grey mohair. We were told not to bring any amplification as the venue had its own, so we just went up there in the Cortina estate and Ray's 1950s Ford Zephyr.

We found the club, a sprauncy place that looked and smelled of money. The two commissionaires, or flash bouncers, who looked as hard as nails, took us into this palace, or that's what it looked like to us. It was out of this world – glitz everywhere. Sammy reared his ugly head with some of his hooligans and started giving out the orders.

Steve laughed and said, 'Who're we playing to – royalty?'

Sammy wasn't impressed and growled back, 'Son, all you're here for is to play, not think. I don't want any heavy music, if you get my meaning.'

Des jumped in. 'Don't worry, Sammy, it'll be everything you want.'

Sammy laughed, which eased the tension. 'Des, are you their bleedin' manager now?' He then clocked Tony, who looked like the wild man of Borneo. 'Is this the new drummer? He looks washed out. You'd better get him spruced up before you start playing otherwise you might have to find another one.' He moved off laughing to himself.

Ray said to Tone, 'He's impressed with you, Tone. I'd go and find a barber if I was you.'

'On your bike.'

The staff and Sammy's crowd were busying themselves getting the place ready for the night. Rick clocked this bird talking to Sammy; she was about 18, a stunner with long dark hair, immaculate make-up and wearing a dark green trouser suit.

'That's one tasty lady over there. I think I'm in love.'

'Do you want to end up in an early grave, Rick?'

'What're you on about, Des?'

'That's Sammy's daughter, Carol. The last bloke who tried his luck with her ended up as bait for the fishermen at the end of Southend pier. She's well out of bounds.'

Why did I think that Rick wasn't going to listen to Des's advice? While we were setting up I had a quiet word with Des about tonight's guest of honour.

'Who are we playing for tonight?'

'Best not to ask, Nick. You've heard that saying "Careless talk cost lives".'

Everything was in place as I viewed the scene. There was enough food and drink to sink a battleship. The decorations could have only come from Harrods. This was the swankiest place we'd ever played by far. To hire this night club for the whole day would've cost thousands. We were set up and sitting on the stage in our new suits and button-down white Fred Perry shirts watching all the guests arrive. As soon as we spotted the first few arrivals we knew this was no ordinary party. All dressed up in smart suits, it looked like a villains' convention. They looked a hard bunch and their ladies had more jewellery than the whole of Hatton Garden.

Des did name some of the faces that came in and what crimes they'd committed. All the boys looked at each other and Steve said worryingly, 'We better be note perfect tonight.'

Ray looked at Steve and laughed. 'You'd better feck off home then.'

'We wouldn't be here if it wasn't for your punch-up.'

Then Sammy came over in a suit so sharp you could've cut your hand on it. Behind him was his daughter, Carol, who looked like a princess in her outfit, which was probably from Biba of Kensington. Brigitte Bardot would have struggled to look like her that night.

Sammy looked at us and said with an air of menace, 'Right, you lot, our special guest will be here in two minutes and this will be the best you've ever played. His daughter will be coming and she likes to sing one or two numbers.'

Rick butted in. 'Do you know what numbers she'll do?'

'What do you think I am, a feckin' mind reader, son? You're the musicians. She'll tell you and you play it. It better be good because our guest has only one daughter and he idolises her, so mess up and, well, I'd hate to think of the consequences.'

I looked at Rick and said, 'Do you know, this sounds all too familiar…'

'What're you on about?'

'Remember when I met you, you had this bird in tow called Andrea. I was playing in a band for her 21st, she got up and sang and cleared the hall out in 10 seconds.'

'Don't remind me – she was chronic.' He grinned and said, 'But she did have a nice pair.'

Carol stayed in the background while her Dad was giving us the verbal. When he'd gone she went over to Rick and said, 'Sorry my Dad was so rude to you.'

'That's OK. Sorry, I didn't get your name.'

'Carol. And yours?'

'It's Rick. I hope you don't mind me saying, but you look gorgeous.'

Suddenly the room of about 200 people went quiet. Monty, looking like an advert for C&A in his new whistle, came through

the door followed by this bloke of about 50. He was a huge man,
about 18 stone and a face as hard as the Rock of Gibraltar. Then
everybody sang 'For he's a jolly good fellow'. We all went cold
as we recognised him. He'd been the subject of a documentary
on television. His picture had been in all the newspapers for the
last few weeks. He had just been released from prison following
the demise of a gangland rival. With my mouth still wide open,
our mate Ronnie came over. He was the original wheeler and
dealer, and looked the part in his black long-jacketed suit, like an
undertaker.

'You're brave, Nick.'

'What d'you mean, Ronnie?'

'Well, all the top bands and even some of the lesser ones like
yours were asked to do this gig, but they all declined when they
knew who it was for.'

'You're joking!'

'I ain't, trust me – it's kosher.'

'I wouldn't trust you, Ronnie, if you were the last person on
earth. By the way, how come you're here?'

'Friends in high places, Nick. Must go. I'll pick up with you
later.'

Carol and Rick were still chatting when she noticed her Dad
coming over to us. She quickly made herself scarce.

'Right you lot – I'll give you the nod in a minute or two.
It better bleedin' be good or you've got me to answer to. And
remember, nothing too heavy.'

A worried Des looked at Rick and said, 'Remember what I said.
Be careful. The fishing season has just started.'

We all had a good laugh that quickly changed to fear as Sammy
gave us the nod to play. Tone is an excellent drummer and he led
us into *I Can't Explain* by the Who, forgetting that Sammy didn't
want any heavy music. From then on we relaxed and it went well
for the first session, so much so that some of the villains even said
how much they were enjoying our music. We found them polite
and respectful, and nobody was making a fool of themselves, but
I would hate to upset them. It was all good news and at the break
lovely nosh and plenty of Dom Perignon champagne – not the

Pomagne we used to have at family parties. What surprised us was that there appeared to be an official photographer in tow who was snapping everyone, including taking photos of us and also some filming. I would've thought they wanted this to be a low-profile affair. On the other hand, any big jobs going off tonight meant they all had their alibis!

We were enjoying the moment when Ray said, 'Christ, look who's walking towards us.'

The guest of honour came over to us and said in a polite but firm voice, 'Enjoying the music, lads, and thanks for playing for me tonight.'

'Our pleasure,' I said.

'Now, I want you to do me a small favour please.'

Des piped up and said, 'Of course – anything you want, Jack.'

'Hello, Des – didn't see you hiding behind that amplifier. Are you and the old man still ringing motors?'

'That's all behind us. Now, what's the favour, Jack?'

We were astounded that he knew the bloke and was on first-name terms.

'My beautiful daughter, Annabel, would like to sing a couple of songs after the break. I'd really appreciate it, as she wants to get into show biz as a singer, and now I'm out I'll be helping her.'

'Take it as read, Jack. Send her over and we'll make sure it happens,' said Des.

'That's great lads. I owe yer.'

As he walked off, I tore into Des. 'What are you on about giving him promises like that? And how is it you're on first-name terms with one of the biggest gangsters in London?'

Before he could say anything, Ray shouted out, 'Tell me this ain't his daughter.'

A girl of about 20 was striding over towards us on a mission. Sammy's daughter Carol was a princess, but this was the frog. She had thighs that a Hereford bull would be proud of. She was a size and certainly wasn't a looker. She went up to Ray, thank goodness, and said in a squeaky voice, 'My Dad said its OK for me to sing a couple of songs after the break.'

Ray coughed and spluttered and said, 'We can't disappoint your

Dad, can we?'

She looked at Ray with piercing eyes and rather cockily said, 'No. My Dad doesn't like disappointments.'

Ray had had enough of her and said angrily, 'So what do you want to sing, then?'

'Two numbers that suit my voice…'

'Two numbers?'

'Is that a problem?' she said snidely.

'What are they then?'

'*Summertime* and *Yesterday*. Do you know them?'

'Just about. What key do you want to sing in?'

She looked vacant. 'What do you mean, key?'

We all sniggered and Ray said, 'You can't just get on the mic and start singing. We need to know a rough idea of what key you're going to sing in.'

'That's your problem. Let me know when you're starting again and we'll do *Yesterday* first.'

With that she stomped off over to her Dad.

Des jumped straight up and said to us, 'Look, you're going to have to put up with this jumped-up little cow. If it all goes wrong you'll get the blame. We know she can't sing, but somehow she's got to sound half decent.'

With Des's words ringing in our ears we quickly went backstage and sorted out the chords and drumbeat. We were going to jazz up the two numbers because if she is chronic we can fizz-up the background and it won't sound so bad. It was agreed that we'd stand by the mics and come in when needed, which would probably be straight away. Fortunately we knew these numbers and in fact sometimes played them when the dancers wanted some smooching. They were ideal for blokes to grab a bird.

Then the serious stuff started when Monty came over to us. His new suit was so shiny you could see your face in it. He said to us, 'Right, lads, first half was good. Jack will be coming over in a minute to have a word with his guests. After he's had a word he wants to introduce his daughter before she gets up and sings.'

Des butted in and said diplomatically, 'Monty, I've heard her singing is that bad she's been entered in the feckin' Eurovision

Song Contest.'

Monty's face was a picture. He dropped his guard and said with a grin, 'Des, if it wasn't so serious I'd laugh my head off, but if you lot don't come up with the goods you'll end up like the other band that backed her a few weeks ago. They had to disband after the gig.'

'Why was that?'

'They found it hard to play guitar and drums with only one hand. Hang about, Jack's coming over.'

Jack took the mic and thanked everybody for coming. His daughter was now on the stage as her father said with pride, 'I'd like to welcome my daughter, Annabel, who is going to sing us a couple of songs. Please give her a great welcome.'

He walked off the stage and all eyes looked towards her. In the break we'd had a word with her about how we were going to play the two numbers and when she should come in. Hopefully she had taken it on board, but I doubted it. Ray gave her the mic and she dropped it. I quickly took my mic off the stand and gave it to her in case she'd broken it. It was a nightmare as we began *Summertime*. Tone gently beat us in and Rick played a long intro, then Annabel started singing. It was like a pig being castrated, and within a few seconds we'd upped the sound and Rick and Ray were singing with her. We went straight in with *Yesterday* and did the same thing on that song. Somehow we pulled it off. She thought she was good and bowed to the audience, who gave her polite applause, only because of her Dad. If it hadn't been for him she would've been sent to the stocks and pelted with eggs.

We got through the night and were pleased with our performance. We thought the suits were cool and wore them as the norm at all our future gigs after that.

While we were packing up Jack came over to us. We shuddered in case he wasn't happy. 'Thanks for playing for me tonight. I thought you were great. What you did for my daughter with those two songs I really appreciate it. In fact, her and her mate would like to be your backing singers, if that's OK.'

Tone dropped one of the cymbals, which made a hell of a noise. Jack then winked and laughed and said, 'Only kidding! She ain't no Helen Shapiro or Sandie Shaw is she? I think she's going to have to find another vocation.'

We politely laughed and just nodded. To our surprise he then pulled out a bundle of notes from his pocket and gave them to me. 'Here's a drink for you all. I gather there were plenty of bands who wouldn't play this party because it was for me. If I can put out any fires for you, just let me know.'

Steve said with a grin, 'What's your name – Red Adair?'

'Yeah, they do call me the fourth emergency service.' Jack burst out laughing and walked off, chuckling to himself.

We were all glad that gig was out of the way and perhaps now we could get back to normality. Mixing with the criminal fraternity had been self-inflicted, so it was time to move on to just playing music. But there was one drawback. Rick was now secretly seeing Sammy's daughter, Carol, behind his back. That was a big no-no. I could only see pain at the end of that road.

We were now off to play a number of universities and colleges, which was a first for us. TJ had certainly got us some different bookings, so we were looking forward to them. The first one was a student union bash on the South Coast. We were met by this hippy-type bird called Penelope Smythe-Barton. I bet her Dad didn't work at Ford's in Dagenham. She said, 'Your manager's office has just rung us with an urgent call. You need to ring Pauline immediately.'

While the other guys humped the gear in, I made the call. I still had the ache with her, but you have to move on.

'What's so urgent that you need to get hold of us, Pauline?'

'Have you seen the national newspapers today?'

'We can't afford newspapers on what TJ pays us.'

'Well, you'd better get hold of one now, because he's after your blood.'

'Hang about! There's a newspaper on the table here. What am I looking for, then?'

'Most of the newspaper headlines are "The bravest band in England". Have you found it yet?'

'What are you on about, Pauline?'

'Just look, Nick.'

I flicked through the paper. On page 5 there was a picture of us in our new suits with the headline, "English band Modern Edge play where others fear…"'

'I'll ring you back, Pauline.'

I rushed off with the newspaper to show the lads. They couldn't believe it. We were made to look brave playing the gig at Monty's party for Jack. We weren't brave, more like stupid. We felt embarrassed and rather foolish about it all. Des went out and got some other newspapers and it was all the same. The only good thing about it was seeing the photo of us in the newspapers, which gave us a buzz, but the rest was pure fiction. I'd like to know who put the bubble into the press about us playing there…

While we were setting up in the hall various office staff from the university kept coming out to us saying such and such wants to speak to you on the phone. We just blanked it and got on with setting up. With about an hour to go we were all ready to play. The students started arriving, and it looked like a fancy dress party – some of them, you wouldn't believe that they were women. I could tell there was a whiff of weed in the air as Tone's nose was twitching, but as long as that was all it was… We were still on a permanent drug alert with him.

With about 500 students ready to party, we plugged in and with the set lists by our side we went straight into our signature tune *Suburban Mod*. We didn't like to rabbit much between numbers so it was music all the way. I have to say we got a great reception, and the first set was cool. At the break a few of the female students came over. We all got stuck in. Tone likes the oddball type and he wasn't disappointed. She was as tall as a giraffe, wore Dr Martins and her clothes were like rags. Her red hair, black lipstick and make-up made her look like a witch, but Tone was happy. That was him sorted for the night. I made a play for Lindy, who seemed keen, and Steve was all over her mate Jill. We arranged to see them after the gig. Rick and Ray, without our knowledge, had pulled two of the office staff before the show. Des and a couple of students were going to pack up the gear for us after the gig. We'd arranged to meet back at our digs in the morning for our next date, which was in Southampton.

The second set was wild and the students knew how to party. What a great night! If these colleges were anything to go by I was looking forward to more of the same. After we'd sweated our bollocks off for two and a half hours on stage we were now on the party trail with the girls for some fun. The two girls took Steve and me to a party that was well heavy with drugs. There were more drugs on show than in Boots. As mentioned, we were an old-fashioned band and drugs didn't do it for us.

After a couple of hours we went back to the girls' flats, which were next door to each other. Lindy took me to her flat and I was now rampant. She was well high on pills and I was high on pints of Red Barrel. She was dancing around the room and started stripping off. This is going to be a night to remember, I said to myself. She's now down to her black bra and knickers and she beckons me towards her. It was so stiff I could hardly walk. Then we started snogging and groping, then she collapsed onto the bed. She was laying there with this funny grin on her face, out for the count. I knew I was a fair snogger but I wasn't that good. I tried to wake her up but it was no good. She was zonked out. I waited a couple of minutes in case she came to, but she didn't, so I put a blanket over her and let myself out.

I thought, it's a long way to walk to the digs on my own! I heard a lot of huffing and puffing from Jill's flat where Steve was. I knocked on the door and shouted to him, 'Steve, I need to talk to you – it's urgent.' There was no answer so I shouted louder. 'Steve, we need to talk.'

Suddenly there was a shuffle and he came to the door in a state of undress. 'What the feck do you want, Nick?'

'Look, I thought I'd better tell you what Lindy has just told me. Jill had a test last week.'

'Well, what's that got to do with me?'

'It was positive.'

'Positive for what?'

'Crabs, and they're feckin' big ones. I thought I'd better let you know. I've left Lindy in bed to come and tell you. She's probably got the right hump with me now. So it's up to you, mate, if you want the umbrella treatment up your old boy. I'm off back to the digs. Good hunting.'

Steve screwed his face up and shut the door. I counted to ten, and on eight he was out of that door a bit lively.

As we walked back to the digs he said, 'Thank goodness you told me. I was just about to dip me wick.'

'Well, that's what friends are for, Steve.'

'I owe you one, Nick – you're a real mate.'

The next gig in Southampton wasn't a college but a dingy dance hall not far from the docks. I spoke to TJ and he was on the warpath following the party for Monty and said in his fanny voice, 'It clearly states in your contract Nick, that you're not allowed any PJs [private jobs], otherwise I can cancel your contract.'

Pauline was turning out to be a real gem for us, as she'd told him that since our band had been plastered all over the newspapers she'd taken a lot more bookings for us. Money talks in TJ's world. He left us alone as he worked out how much more money he could make out of us. The good news was that Pauline had agreed to have a drink with me when we got back home.

This place in Southampton was a dump and we wondered why our management was making us play here. It was called College Hall and I bet he'd put two and two together and come out with five! But they must have been paying the right money, so the gig had to be done. It wasn't a bad night and the customers seemed to like us, we thought. At the end of the evening we were putting the gear back in the van when about eight blokes confronted us. This sometimes happens, as their girls often make comments about the band and their blokes get jealous. I did notice Batman and Robin, aka Rick and Ray, chatting up a couple of girls, so maybe their blokes wanted a bit of retribution. One of them, a horrible-looking mutt with tattoos, greasy hair and a gut that looked like a ten-pint-a-night job, stepped forward and said, 'So you lot are the bravest band in England, eh?'

The newspaper articles were going to be the death of us. Everywhere we went we were going to be offered up for a punch-up. We just ignored him and got on with loading up.

He got nearer and gobbed off again. 'I'm talking to you lot.'

Ray, looking angry, stepped forward and said, 'Piss off, you big, fat, ugly bastard.'

'What did you say?'

'Do you want me to repeat it, you dickhead?'

With that the bloke tried to lay a punch on Ray. Now, as we know, Ray is a boxer and he's good – in fact, very good. He chinned the bloke, then hit him in the gut, he puked everywhere, and fell to the ground in a daze. The others were coming towards us for revenge. Suddenly Des appeared from the back of the van like one of the Three Musketeers with the biggest sword you've ever seen. Shouting like a lunatic, he started swinging this sword amongst them. They were petrified and ran off in all directions. Des always kept that sword in the van and it did come in handy sometimes, like that night.

After the tour, which went well, we were all having a greasy in Monty's when Ronnie walked in as large as life. He'd got this black crombie on, a black leather pork pie hat and dark shades.

In his strong cockney accent he said, 'Hello, my sons, how's it going then?'

'Christ, Ronnie, is it Halloween already?' I said.

'Cheeky sod! This crombie is real schmutter, straight out of the Albert Docks yesterday.'

'Is there a clothes shop down there then?' said Rick, taking the rise.

'Funny, funny… My brother's a docker down there and he's always getting gear out.'

'Is that the same brother who every day for a month wheeled out an empty wheelbarrow and they couldn't find out what he was nicking?' said Steve.

'No, that was my other brother, Tommy. He would put his tuck box and flask on the barrow and wheel it home. Security would go over the barrow with a fine tooth comb. One day they even had the wheel off to see whether he was hiding drugs.'

'What was he thieving then?' said Ray, who hadn't heard the story before.

'Feckin' wheelbarrows! You can't make it up, can you?'

We all roared with laughter and Ronnie sat down and had a cup tea with us. Then he dropped a bombshell. 'Nice bit of publicity with all your boat races in the papers. That must have helped get a few more punters through the door.'

'I'd like to know who tipped off the press,' said Tony.

'You're looking at him.'

'Why'd you do that Ronnie?' I asked.

'The power of the press and television, Nick. It's all about being seen and heard. You'll thank me when you're famous. Stand on me, I know all about publicity. I'll soon get you on *Opportunity Knocks*.'

'Oh, leave it out, will yer?' said Ray.

There was a golden silence for just a few seconds before Steve said, 'Hang about, Ronnie – you mentioned television.'

'I forgot to tell yer lads. If you look on the box at nine o'clock Tuesday night you might have a surprise, that's all I'm saying. Right, whose turn is it to get the teas in then?'

As Rick made his way to the counter to get the teas, Ronnie got up and whispered in his ear. 'Rick, my son, be very careful with Carol. If Sammy finds out that the Casanova of Romford is trying to get into his daughter's knickers, he'll go garrity. Remember, he plays with sawn-offs.'

We all gathered round at Rick's house on Tuesday night to see what Ronnie was on about. The family had a brand-new Mitsubishi 22-inch colour TV. I still had a black and white Bush with a screen just a bit bigger than a postage stamp. It was nice to see his Mum and Dad again. Mind you, the old man did rip the band off a few years back, but that's water under the bridge. We sat there with our Woodbines and Watney Party Sevens, then the documentary programme, came on. As soon as we saw it we all uttered four-letter words. It was the continuation of Jack coming out of prison. After a few minutes of backfill from the previous programme the new one started. Ten minutes in we were utterly gobsmacked when the film of his party was shown. The camera panned around the room with all the guests enjoying themselves. Then it went on to Jack who was waving and jumping up and down to the camera. Then it panned onto us and we were full on playing *Jumpin' Jack Flash* by the Rolling Stones. As it happens, it was a real edge seeing ourselves close-up on television, and we lapped it up.

After the programme finished Des said with a grin, 'You know, this was a put-up-job. The producer and director of the film is an old school mate of Jack's. He was well lubricated for his trouble.'

'What do you mean?' I asked.

'Think about it. The programme didn't actually slag off Jack. In the end there was doubt about whether he'd committed the crime he was banged up for. Also, Ronnie came over to you and asked you to play *Jumpin' Jack Flash*. Has the penny dropped yet?'

'Of course! He was seen on film jumping up and down to the song,' Tone said.

'It was two fingers up to authority. You're all a bit slow. Thank goodness there's some brains on the road with you lot,' said cocky Des.

♫ 12 ♫

Rockin' into the Seventies

In 1970 the first Glastonbury Festival was held by Michael Eavis. The same year the Beatles split up, the first Page 3 girl appeared in the *Sun* and the 10-bob note ceased to be legal tender. It was the start of the groovy Seventies and Modern Edge was still on a mission to get that No 1 hit.

After our appearance on television, people came out of the woodwork. Anita from Reading tried to get in touch with me through TJ but I didn't want any more hassle from her and that toe rag of a boyfriend, Simon. Ann from Hull, who I'd met at the holiday camp, gave me a bell. Her alopecia was not an issue any more and her new-felt confidence meant she didn't always wear a wig. We were playing Hull soon, so we were going to meet up.

The terrible twins, Mandy and Viv, went over to Spain to work, but before they went Steve and I enjoyed a weekend with them – we're still getting over it! Billy, our former drummer, had fallen on his feet. He was now engaged to Gloria and living with her in Suffolk and, even better news, the band he joined had got a record deal. We felt that, as a band, we'd done our best to get a new record deal but it hadn't happened. So it was more touring, which we love, then hopefully somebody would pick us up.

TJ was still booking the gigs for us – he was now a major player in the music business. When there was a problem with some of his bands, which seemed to be all the time, he got in touch with us. For instance, we played at Barnstaple in Devon one Saturday night. We got a call from him that one of his bands had had a big bust-up and they'd jacked it in. On the Sunday night they were playing a big gig in Sunderland. So what happened after the Barnstaple job? We travelled through the night all the way to Geordie-land and filled in for them!

Dagenham band the Senators pose on the roof of the Circus
Tavern, Purfleet, while playing a gig in 1964. From left to right,
they are Alan Moss (lead guitar), Dave Birch (drummer), Steve ?
(bass), Stuart ? (singer) and David Buthlay (rhythm guitar). *David
Buthlay collection*

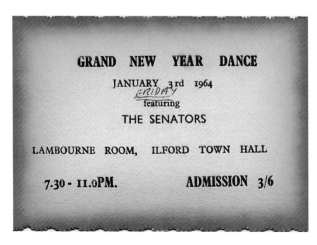

A dance
ticket.
How
prices have
changed!
*David
Buthlay
collection*

The Sixties Boys Rock The 70s

The Senators at the Circus Tavern in 1964. Note the Vox amps in the foreground. *David Buthlay collection*

Opposite top: Quota Plus from Chelmsford, Essex, with whom the author played in the 1970s. Left to right, they are Dave Hughes (keyboards), David Buthlay (lead guitar), Brian Rowland (drummer), Dave Moore (singer) and Alan Hammond (bass guitar). *F. W. Tyler*

Opposite bottom: In 2013 Quota Plus had a reunion for the first time in nearly 40 years. Left to right are Dave Hughes, David Buthlay, Alan Hammond and Brian Rowland. Unfortunately Dave Moore couldn't be traced. *Chrissie Hammond*

The Sceptres playing at the Fishing Smack pub in Barking in the mid-1960s. The line up, from left to right, is Alan Moss (lead guitar), Dave Worral (bass), Bernie Lawrence (vocalist), Pete ? (drummer) and David Buthlay (rhythm guitar). *David Buthlay collection*

The Sabres about to play at Whitley's cafe, Huddersfield, for a company Christmas party. Left to right, they are drummer Brian Fearnley, bass Roy Walton, rhythm guitar Alan Wadsworth, lead vocals Peter Lee and lead guitar Dave Thorp. *Peter Lee collection*

Photographed at Penistone Town Hall on a New Year's Eve during the 1960s are, left to right, Brian Fearnley, Roy Walton, Peter Lee and Dave Thorp, rocking with their band Lee Stuart and the Sabres. *Peter Lee collection*

How many bands can say they have played together for more than 50 years? Well, the Sabres can, seen here playing at Penistone bowling club in Yorkshire at a Tour de France event in the summer of 2014. Left to right are bassist Roy Walton, singer Peter Lee, drummer Robert Drummond, with the band for two years, and guitarist and another original member David Thorp. *Peter Lee collection*

A 1960s calling card for Lee Stuart and the Sabres. *Peter Lee collection*

ENTERTAINMENT VALUE
AND SATISFACTION
SUPPLIED BY

LEE STUART AND THE SABRES

TELEPHONE :
PENISTONE 3383.

HEADQUARTERS :
WENTWORTH ARMS HOTEL,
PENISTONE.

The Blue Stripes from mid-Sussex, seen in 1963. Left to right are Adrian, Ralph Pendry, Mick and Ken. The boys supported such bands as the John Barry Seven and Georgie Fame and the Blue Flames. *Ralph Pendry collection*

Christine Hughes, Mod girl of the '60s, has her photo taken before going to the Kursaal dance hall in Southend in 1964. *Bill Hughes*

A rare Mott the Hoople poster from 15 November 1973. The support band was Queen. Christopher Nicholson remembers, 'Two of us from Worcester College were hired as extra "roadies" for the evening, unloading and loading the equipment from the vans and helping set up. We had an hour in a local pub after the sound check for the "support group", where I remember thinking how "strange" the lead singer was – although when I heard his voice during the concert I was very impressed! I remember him singing Shirley Bassey's *Hey Big Spender*. This was Queen's only tour as "support" group in the UK – after this I think they went with Mott the Hoople to tour America, then ... the rest is history. I have a signed photo poster of Mott the Hoople from that evening, but couldn't be bothered to get the "support" to sign it!

At a Rod Stewart and the Faces concert at the Taunton Odeon
on 3 December 1974, in the first picture Rod is on the left, while
Ian McLagan plays his Steinway piano. In the second picture Rod
is seen again, with drummer Kenny Jones in the background, and

in the third Ronnie
Wood and Rod share
the vocals.

Photographer
Christopher Nicholson
recalls that it was
'…a cold but dry
night. There was a
long queue to get
in. I hid my 35mm
SLR camera with
telephoto lens under
my coat until we
reached our seats in
the balcony, which
had a good view of the
stage. On came the

support group called "Strider" (I think) followed by a long, long interval. This was not unusual at Faces concerts (I recall a similar experience from the previous year's Faces concert at Worcester Gaumont on 3 December 1973, where I also took photos, two of which appeared in Alan's book *The Sixties Boys on Tour*. Eventually the Faces appeared and started with *It's All Over Now* followed by a selection of popular and not so well-known Faces songs and Rod

Stewart hits – but not *Maggie May*, which appeared in the set lists for previous concerts of the same tour. I started taking photos from the balcony and was never challenged. Even with stage lights it was difficult. They finished with *Twistin' the Night Away* at about 10.30pm, just in time for some people's last bus home – in the days when there were still last buses at that time! A jolly good time was had by all – the Faces and the audience!

The set list was *It's All Over Now, Take a Look at the Guy, I'm Losing You, Bring It On Home To Me/You Send Me, Sweet Little Rock 'n' Roller, I'd Rather Go Blind, Angel, Stay With Me/Gasoline Alley,/ Amazing Grace/Stay With Me, Too Bad/Every Picture Tells a Story, Mine For Me, You Can Make Me Dance, Sing or Anything, I Can Feel the Fire, Twistin' the Night Away.*

The Taunton Odeon is now a bingo hall. *Both Christopher Nicholson*

Red Price, on the left, was one of the finest UK rock and roll
saxophone players and session musicians.

  Christopher Nicholson: 'Red Price, a very interesting (and
talented) session musician, once spent several nights at our house
in Sheffield (he and my Dad had served together in the Royal
Navy during the war). I recall one visit when he was backing
Helen Shapiro in March 1963, and a little-known group called
the Beatles were also on the bill. Dad took my brother and me
to meet 'Reg' (his real name) at the City Hall and we got a tour
backstage and in the dressing rooms. I was shown into a dressing
room with half a dozen people, four of whom had "smart suits"
on. One of them offered to sign my autograph book for me. I had
a short conversation with the man – how old was I, did I like pop
music, how did I know Reg, etc? My autograph book was signed,
Reg was needed on stage, and we left. When I got home I asked
my Mum to 'read' the autographs I had collected. One said "Best
wishes John Lennon", she told me, to which I remembered asking,
"Who's John Lennon?" I still have the autograph!

This shot shows Reg in later life performing (I think) at the Batley Variety Club or a small jazz club in Leeds where he ended up in later life teaching others how to play the saxophone. His claim to fame was that he played the *Danger Man* theme from the 1960s TV programme, backed Eddie Cochran on several UK TV appearances in early 1960, and was also the lead saxophonist in Lord Rockingham's XI – remember the 1958 No 1 *Hoots Mon*?

A Rolls Royce Phantom VI with a 1974/75 registration plate. *Alan Hammond*

Ivan Bluffield, with his red Austin A40 Farina, is seen at the idyllic Alma Villa farmhouse in Curry Rivel, Somerset, in 1965. *Jill Bluffield*

A lovely photo of a 1932 Morris Minor taken in 1955 at Oaklands Road, Enfield Highway, with the owner, Leslie Bluffield, on his way to work as a rep. *Ivan Bluffield collection*

A great picture of a Ford Zephyr taken in 1953. *Peter Triggs collection*

Vespas on the move in the 1960s. *Peter Triggs collection*

Musical icons of the '60s, '70s and beyond with the author.

The brilliant Phil Collins, now back performing across the world.
Steve Guscott

Rod Stewart, one of the best-selling artists of all time. *Chrissie Hammond*

Jools Holland, founding member of '70s band Squeeze. *Chrissie Hammond*

Michael Eavis, founder of the Glastonbury Festival. *Steve Guscott*

Dave Berry, who had a big hit in 1964 with *The Crying Game*. *Chrissie Hammond*

Sir Richard Branson launched his first record label, Virgin Records, in 1972. *Steve Guscott*

Marty Wilde, who kindly wrote the Foreword for my book *Sixties Boys Unzipped*. *Chrissie Hammond*

The author with fashion icon Jeff Banks. He was once married to pop star Sandie Shaw. *Alan Hammond collection*

Tony Christie had a massive hit with *Is This The Way To Amarillo* in 2005, when it reached No 1, having been first released in 1971. *Chrissie Hammond*

Hammond banned for 5 weeks

Alan Hammond, Rainham left-back, has been suspended for five weeks. The suspension, imposed by the F.A. last week, started yesterday.

Hammond, 20, was sent off four weeks ago in the Essex Senior Cup replay at East Ham after being booked in three previous matches.

The sending-off led him to have his long hair cut because he felt referees were penalising his appearance almost as much as his football behaviour.

Says Larry Hutson, Rainham manager: "I'm not surprised by the length of the suspension, only pleased it wasn't longer."

● HAMMOND

A newspaper cutting from 1969, describing of one of the author's unfortunate football misdemeanours.

I met up with Pauline and we saw each other when we could, so that was back on. We'd kept out of Monty's cafe for a bit as we didn't want to be sucked into any more iffy situations. The line-up of the band was still the same. Tone appeared not to have gone back on drugs, so that was a real bonus. Rick was now bonking Sammy's daughter, Carol, on a regular basis. I hated to think what would happen if her old man found out, because he'd murder Rick, literally. They'd used my place a few times, which I was going to have to put a stop to as I didn't want to be an accessory to a murder! Ray was offered a singing job with a top-rate band on a lot more money, but stayed loyal to us.

We met with TJ every three months, when he'd give us the low down on what future gigs were booked – and we liked to make sure that our wages were going up, not down. To be fair, on that front we didn't have any troubles, but he did throw them in and one was coming our way right now.

'Nick, did you get in touch with Anita?' asked TJ. 'She's been on the horn three times and she seems upset.'

'Yeah, Steve and I were upset being beaten up by their boyfriends and their mates. One day we'll get even with them. There'll be a comeback when they least expect it.'

'I'm with yer there, Nick,' said Steve.

'Don't get involved – it'll only end in tears.'

'For them it will, TJ,' I said.

'Right – down to business. I need a favour from you lot.'

'Is it a paying favour?' asked Ray.

'Yeah don't worry – you'll earn. Listen up – I've got a new prodigy under my wing called Tammy.'

'More like under your bed,' said Rick with a laugh.

'This is purely business. Christ, will you lot listen up? You know you've got a top-rated gig in Camden in two weeks' time. I want her to do half a dozen numbers there and I want you to back her.'

'We're not a backing band,' said Tone.

'I'd keep schtum if I was you, Tony. As far as I'm concerned you're still on probation for giving aspirin a run for their money.'

'Piss off! I'm off drugs – that's all in the past.'

I jumped straight in. I was well annoyed with him. 'That's out

of order. We only work for you – you don't own us. Any more of
that and you can poke your agency right up your arse.'

It all went quiet as we eyeballed him. His bottle went. 'Perhaps
I was out of order. Sorry, Tone.'

'Well out of order. Now, what's this favour you want?' I asked.

'As I said, I would like her to sing a few numbers. I've booked
the hall in Elm Park for three days to go over the numbers she's
going to sing. She lives up your way in Chadwell Heath, so it all
fits in.'

He went over a few more details and, as we were getting paid
for the rehearsing and the gig, we had no problem. His last words
to us as we left the building were, 'I don't want any of you lot
trying to get your leg over with her.'

We'd practised at Elm Park before, so we got there early and
set up ready for this new sensation that TJ was pinning his hopes
on. What riled us was that he'd reckoned he'd got her a record
deal, but there was still no deal for us. We worked on a few new
numbers while we waited. Suddenly TJ appeared wearing a union
jack suit with bell-bottom trousers and a jacket to match – a clown
would have been happy to wear it. He'd dyed his hair white and
had this silly baker's boy hat on, normally worn by women. He
came over to us, gave a twirl and said,
'Like the gear? I bought this from John Stephen. It's all the range
in Carnaby Street.'

'I think I'll stick with John Collier in the High Street,
Romford,' said Ray with a laugh.

We all stopped and looked towards the door as Tammy walked
in. I don't know what we were expecting. She was a girl of about
our age, short fair hair and dressed in a dark red trouser suit,
average looks, but what an arse on it! She introduced herself and
appeared to have plenty of confidence. She said with an air of
arrogance, 'You're my backing band, then?'

Ray jumped straight in with, 'Yeah, one night only.'

'Oh, you promised me my own band, TJ.'

Looking totally flustered, he quickly said, 'I'm in the process of
interviewing musicians for your new band right now, sweetheart.'

'Dinky and the Dynamos are available,' said Steve, as we all laughed.

She was going to sing about six covers so there was no new material. They were bog standard numbers and not very inspiring. We went through the numbers with her and to be honest she wasn't that good. Plenty of hip swinging, lots of smiles, but her singing was just average. After a couple of hours the band was bored and just went through the motions with her. TJ had already gone, so he couldn't hear the six numbers being beaten to death. We only spent another day with her – we couldn't take any more. We arranged to see her early at the show in Camden the following week. We'd rather do more work with her there than a church hall with no heating. TJ brought her in his motor, but Ray quickly volunteered to take her home. I wonder why…

During the week I met up with Terry from the Tanks. I told him about this bird Tammy and he started laughing and said, 'You must be the only band in Essex who ain't backed her. She goes from manager to manager because she's tone deaf when it comes to music. The only good thing about her is her arse.'

'Have you backed her?'

'Yeah, at a gig in Harlow. She was chronic. They booted her and us off stage. Never again.'

'We're backing her at a show in Camden next week.'

'That's a great venue to play. They won't like her there. You'd better have a plan B.'

I did bell TJ and tried, diplomatically, to tell him that Camden was not the place to try her out. I suggested a pub in Stratford where they're too hammered to worry about who is singing. He wasn't impressed and put the phone down. Later that day Steve came round and we had a pow-wow. The band was concerned that our gigs were now not getting as many people through the door as we used to. In fact, it was tailing off to a point where we were worried that TJ might pull the plug on us. The music was much more progressive now, with bands like Electric Light Orchestra, Mott the Hoople, Queen, Pink Floyd, Genesis and Led Zeppelin, to name a few, leading the way. Lots of '60s bands were now old hat and had either packed up or had made line-up changes with hardly any of the existing band members left. We were purely a

'60s band – did we want to change our style of music to stay in the game? All these questions had to be asked.

I said to Steve, 'Is it time to re-invent ourselves?'

'Into what, Nick? We're good enough musicians to change our style of music, but is that what we really want? I don't know, but I do appreciate that something has got to be done.'

'It's unlikely that a record company will take us on board with music that's going out of fashion.'

'So we're still the travelling jukebox playing all the '60s music until we come up with an answer, or the answer is made up for us, Steve.'

'Do you know, it's times like this that I miss Mandy and Viv. They make you forget about everything except for the S word. By the way, any runners and riders in the black book, Nick?'

'Well, as it happens, remember those two birds we saw at the Ilford Palais when we had a night off? Well, we never belled them.'

'Right, what's their number Nick? Let's give them a tinkle. We need a bit of female company.'

The Camden gig was upon us and we were setting up. The thought of backing Tammy had given me sleepless nights. Ray, on the other hand, was as happy as Larry. He'd crept into her bed and they were all over each other.

I said to Ray, 'Can't you use your charm and get her to give tonight a miss?'

'Her singing isn't that bad.'

'You're having a laugh, Ray! The Salvation Army wouldn't even have her singing in their ranks.'

For whatever reason the band didn't seem focused that night. It was a real coup to play there – everybody seemed to be laid back. Rick walked in holding hands and slobbing over Carol, Sammy's daughter. Her old man still didn't know they were an item. Sammy's nickname was 'sawn-off' – I'll leave that to your imagination. Tone came in and looked spaced out. I hoped he hadn't been on the wacky baccy again. He looked rubbish and putting his drum set together seemed an effort for him. When Tammy walked in, looking like mutton dressed up as lamb, wearing more make-up than a clown, Ray sprang into action. He was like a dog on heat, forgetting we had to have a sound check. Even Des was below par. He was complaining of pains in his stomach, so much so that he couldn't lump the gear in. We were playing three sets and Tammy would be on in the second. TJ was there looking proudly at his next sensation. But once he heard her singing he'd get crushed in the rush for the door.

About 10 minutes before lift-off I was looking at the 200 or so people coming in. I was surprised – they weren't teeny-boppers but a more mature crowd.

The first set was horrendous. I'd never known it as bad as that. Rick and Ray were more concerned at grinning at their loved ones than concentrating on what we were playing. Tone was late on nearly every number; I thought he was going to keel over at one point. Steve and I tried to keep it together but it was chronic. We survived the first set and the audience gave us a good cheer and a few whistles when we came off stage. I then lost it when we got back to the dressing room, and turned on Rick and Ray.

'You two were a joke! Your singing was rubbish, Ray, and if that was playing keyboards, Rick, then I suggest you go and play with Dinky – he's looking for some new band members. And you can join him as well, Tone. If you're back on drugs you can leave now and we'll find somebody else.'

Rick went into one with me and said, 'That's well out of order, volleying us! You're not our manager.'

'That's right,' said Ray. 'You can't tell us what to do, so cobblers.'

'That's fine by me. Perhaps it's time we pulled the plug on the band because I'm not having this. Remember, this is our job, and we get paid for it. We all like girls but as soon as it interferes with work then it's a no-no.'

'I agree with Nick,' said Steve. 'That was the worst set we've ever played, so perhaps we should go our separate ways.'

TJ then burst through the door, followed by Tammy, and spouted off. 'That was diabolical – you play like that any more and you can find yourself a new manager. How can I let Tammy down with you lot backing her?'

'Do us a favour and get somebody else to do it, because with her up front on the second set there'll be a riot,' I said.

'Don't talk about my girlfriend like that!' piped up Ray.

'Your prick is ruling your brain, Ray,' Steve said.

Tammy started crying, then Carol ran in and shouted at Rick. 'Dad is here – what am I going to do? He'll kill us!'

She then started crying uncontrollably, Rick went as white as a sheet, then Tone fell off his chair, looking zonked out. We'd only got 5 minutes before we were back on set. Des stepped in, clearly in pain. 'What's wrong with you lot? You're pushing the self-destruct button. You're acting like idiots! There's a gig to play, so get out there and do the business and give this poor girl a chance. None of you are perfect – Tammy needs your help, so give it to her.'

When Des says something everybody listens. He doesn't say a lot, but when he does, most of the time it makes sense. The whole room went quiet when suddenly the buzzer went for the next set. Because I'd gobbed off in the first place, I felt it was right I should say something. I looked at Tammy and said, 'I apologise. We'll make it work for you, so don't worry. And the rest of you – let's get back on stage.'

It was a tense moment as we went back out. We'd never fallen out like that before. Tammy had composed herself, I gave her a smile and we began. Everybody was focused and the set went well. Tammy pulled it off and so did the band. All our aggression came out in the last set and we let it rip. From a crap beginning we got the audience off their feet – they wanted more and they got it.

As we cleared the gear off the stage at the end of the night there was still an uneasy atmosphere between us. Living in each other's pockets for six years, it was bound to happen. It was a good thing we had a week off before a two week mini-tour up North. Hopefully it would all blow over.

Fortunately Sammy didn't catch his daughter and Rick. In fact, he wasn't there for that. He had mates in North London, so he was there for the music. It was a close call, so they both eased off seeing each other for a bit! Ray and Tammy were going out until she asked him to play in her new band, as he's an excellent keyboard player and, of course, singer. He politely said no, and she

jacked him in. She was going on tour in a few weeks' time with
her new band. I was glad it wasn't us. Tone said he wasn't back
on drugs at Camden – he'd had a late night, so that was why he
seemed out of it. I had my doubts, so he needed to be kept an eye
on. I felt sometimes like a mother hen, but you can't let things
slide otherwise it'll grind to a halt. After a few months, Tammy
broke away from TJ and signed up with another manager.

I went round to see Steve and his Dad, Tom, who wanted a
word with us about the accounts. He looked after all of that for us
and the bottom line was that we were just about breaking even. He
said that if we were a business we'd probably have to think about
jacking it in. The only asset was our equipment, but except for our
guitars and keyboard, which were worth a few quid, the rest of the
assets were about 3 bob's worth! It all needed to be replaced. Some
of it was on HP, so we were in the red. That top spot in the charts
was a distant dream. Steve and I were still lucky as we had our
royalties from *Suburban Mod*, the last cheque having gone towards
the Black Maria. Tom had worked out that the gigs for the next
six months would make no difference to our cash flow; in fact,
we'd probably be well in the red. The thought of going back to a
nine-to-five job and not being in the band wasn't worth thinking
about. Somehow we'd got to turn around our fortunes. I knew
that TJ couldn't get any more gigs than he was getting, so we had
to get some more gigs ourselves, and top the money up that way.
Everyone had understanding parents except for me. I'd lost both
mine a while back. We were now in our 20s and you couldn't keep
taking subs off them.

Suddenly the phone rang, and we all jumped. Tom answered it.

'The call is for you, Nick, and it's urgent.'

It was Des's Dad, Frank.

'Right, Steve and I are on our way, Mr Smith.' I looked at Steve
and said, 'Des has collapsed – he's in a bad way. He's been rushed
to Oldchurch hospital in Rush Green.'

Des was in intensive care. We met his Dad there, who told us
what had happened.

'Des has been complaining of a stomach ache for days. This
morning he just keeled over in extreme pain. I dialled three nines

and he's now on the operating table. Another problem – I'm on bail and I've got to report to City Row police station next week. Who's going to look after Des if they take my bail away and remand me?'

'Don't worry, Mr Smith, we'll look after him,' Steve said.

Des was on the operating table for 4 hours. He'd had a burst appendix and they'd also found he'd got an ulcer – probably too many greasy spoons at Monty's. Once we knew he was OK we went home. The next day the band went to visit him and he was sitting up, but still in pain.

He said to us, 'Sorry about all this, but it does mean I can't work. I should be back in about a month's time.'

We'd forgotten about work, being more concerned about our mate Des.

He added, 'I couldn't let you down so I've got a replacement for you.'

'Who's that then, Des?' asked Ray.

'Ronnie.'

'Ronnie? You haven't had a brain op as well?' exclaimed Rick.

'Ronnie's all right. He needs to disappear from his local haunts for a while so it'll do him a favour.'

'Des, he's a liability!' I said. 'You've heard that saying "Lock-up your daughters"? With him, its lock up your possessions. Remember, we're going up North. What are they going to make of him?'

'I'm a bit tired now. Dad has given him the keys to the van and he'll be round early Saturday morning to pick up the equipment from Steve's. Then it's straight up to Hull for the first gig.'

'That's four days away. He'll have sold it by then,' said Tone.

Des's Dad went to City Row to answer bail, but the charges had been dropped so there was someone to look after him. His Mum had died when he was young, but her sister was there for him as well.

The shock of Des and a few days' rest had cleared the air with the band, so hopefully we'd be firing on all cylinders. The thought of Ronnie being the roadie and driver didn't even bear thinking about.

Never again, Ronnie

It was early Saturday morning and we were off to Hull. We were all waiting outside Steve's for Ronnie to turn up in the van to load up. Suddenly a vision appeared in the shape of which I later found out was a blue Mercedes-Benz 0319 bus. Down our road it was only Ford Cortinas, which were nicknamed Dagenham dustbins as everybody worked at Ford's. This was certainly a first for our street, so we enviously looked to see whose house it was going to. It screeched to a halt next to us. Ronnie was in the driver's seat with a silly grin on his face. He jumped out, looking more like a gangster than a gangster, and said, 'Sweet, ain't it?'

'Where'd you get that from?' I asked.

'I got it from a car dealer mate who had a snatch-back, and as he owes me he's let me have it for two weeks. I'm not driving that Black Maria about – I'll lose my cred on the street. So load up and let's get on the motorway.'

'Hang about! Who's picking up the tab for this?'

'Don't worry, Nick, this is on the house. I've had it off on a few deals lately, so everything's cosy. I've also got a bit of business up North so I'll kill two birds with one stone.'

'Ronnie, you never do something for nothing – there's got to be a catch,' said Steve.

'Stand on me – this is a freebie, so let's load up.'

The front of the bus had plenty of seats and at the back our gear easily fitted in. We still took the Cortina, which Tone drove, while the rest of us travelled in the bus. I felt uneasy about all of this as Ronnie was somewhere between a conman and a crook. Something was going off and, knowing Ronnie, he wouldn't be giving up two weeks of his time for nothing.

The bus flew up to Hull – what a smooth ride it was! It made a change not having your body shake, rattle and roll in the Black

Maria. We made good time for the gig that night, which was a 300-seat theatre. To be fair to Ronnie, he got stuck in and we unloaded our gear in record time. He'd done some band work before so he knew the ropes. The manager of the theatre came over to us when we first arrived and asked if Ronnie was with us, as he said he looked like a thug and felt uneasy with him around the theatre. He was spot on. Tongue in cheek, I said to him, 'He's our insurance that we always get paid.'

Ronnie left us a bit lively after the gear was set up just before two look-alike Northern villains arrived. We didn't see him until Monday, because we'd got word from Pauline that our next gig had been cancelled due to poor ticket sales. No wonder, a mega-band was playing the same town, so another cock-up with the management. We had Sunday off, and the theatre management said we could leave our gear there till Monday morning, which was handy as we didn't want anybody trying to nick it out of the bus.

I'd rang Ann up before we went. We'd met her and her mates at the holiday camp at Sidmouth the previous year and, as they lived in the town, it would be great to see them again. She said they were all coming. I saw Ann before the show and the wig was a distant memory as we shared a coffee together at the Mamba coffee bar. She was bubbly and we shared our news. She had a boyfriend, but nothing too serious. It was arranged that after the show Steve and I would meet her and Julie, the girl Steve went out with, for a coffee afterwards.

The theatre had a nice feel to it, which might sound a bit stupid, but you do get a sixth sense about places you play at. You know when there could be trouble and you're on your guard when it doesn't feel right. We put our clobber on and made for the stage. They had their own soundman, a girl student from a college. She knew her music and the sound was great. As we hit the stage we could see Ann, Julie and their mates in the front row and they gave us a great welcome. The theatre was very compact and you felt like you were playing in your own front room. I looked at the other lads as we plugged in and got ready for the concert. We were lucky – all of us loved what we did, and as musicians you have to have that.

That night was one of those occasions where we kept grinning at each other. I don't know why, but you do. We looked like kids bouncing about the stage with silly grins. However, it soon stopped when Steve, who is sillier than most, caught his 12-inch winkle-picker around the lead on my guitar as we were playing *Blackberry Way* by the Move and went arse-over-tit onto Ray, who fell over and dislodged Rick's keyboard. What a shambles! We looked like clowns! The song came to an abrupt end and the crowd were taking the piss, shouting 'More, more!' Thank goodness, it was the last number of the first set. In the dressing room everybody tore into Steve, telling him what a jod he was. The theatre manager came in laughing and said, 'The comedy was better than the music, lads! Got any more of that tucked away?'

It was the first time I'd seen Steve lost for words. The second set there was no more grinning and no more prancing about the stage like demented chickens. At the end of the night we got plenty of applause and did a couple of extra numbers, which went down well.

Not having to play for 48 hours meant it was party time. Steve and I were sorted with our girls and the others were doing their own thing. We'd got digs and it was agreed that we'd be back at the theatre at 9 o'clock Monday to load up the gear and head for Goole, our next port of call.

We met Ann and Julie after the show and the night changed dramatically when Julie said, with a twinkle in her eye, 'Coffee in the Mamba or my house?'

There wasn't any humming or harring from us as Steve and I said simultaneously, 'Your place.'

Julie had an Austin 1100 and, with Steve in the front and Ann and me in the back, we headed for her place. This was handsome – not many girls had cars, so we were as chuffed as an escaped turkey at Christmas. I put my arm around Ann and had a little snog. We arrived at the house, a detached place on a new estate.

Steve said to Julie, 'Won't your Mum and Dad mind us coming round?'

'They won't know. They've gone away for the weekend. They're not back till Monday.'

Steve grinned and looked at me. This was getting better and better.

Julie pulled into the driveway and within minutes we were in the lounge listening to music on her new Fidelity record player. The coffee was forgotten when she took a bottle of Blue Nun out of the fridge and poured generous measures of it into some nice goblets. Then Julie warned, 'No smoking and don't leave any tell-tale evidence that we've had you round here.'

We had a little dance to *Make It With You* by Bread, which got the sap rising as we started on the second bottle of Blue Nun. Julie seemed pretty forward and Steve didn't need much encouragement. Ann seemed a bit nervous as she sipped her wine. Suddenly Julie grabbed Steve and took him upstairs. As she was going she turned round to us and said, 'You can have the spare bedroom. I'll leave the door open so you know which one.'

When they had gone Ann looked at me and I could see she was uncomfortable with it all. I said to her, 'Look, Ann, I can see spending the night with me is maybe a step too far for you. If you want to, you can have the bed upstairs and I'll sleep on the sofa.'

'That's sweet of you, Nick. Look, I have to be honest. I've never done it before and I'm scared.'

'That's OK. Nor have I.'

She gently pushed me and laughed as she said, 'I bet!'

The next morning the household was woken up by the chime of the door bell. Julie flew out of the bedroom like a bat out of hell and said to us in a panic, 'Don't say a word, especially you, Steve, with your gob.'

Her dressing gown was tied tightly as she rushed down the stairs. Steve joined me and Ann in our room. Ann put her head under the sheets as Steve and I peeped through the curtains.

'It's the Old Bill,' said an alarmed Steve.

We automatically thought that Ronnie had been up to his old tricks. We could hear a woman officer talking to Julie downstairs. Ann came up for air and soon disappeared back under the sheets as Steve gave her a grin. The conversation lasted a couple of minutes, then the front door closed. The three of us, in a state of undress, rushed down the stairs as Julie put the kettle on. Steve couldn't contain himself.

'What was all that about, Julie?'

'Nothing to worry about. Just the local police making sure I was all right.'

'Why should they do that then?'

With a cheeky grin she said, 'Didn't I tell you, Steve? My dad's their Chief Inspector – he must have asked them to keep an eye on me while he's away, making sure I'm not having a wild party with some randy bloke from Essex who's trying to get me into bed.'

Steve went as white as a sheet, as he normally does on hearing bad news, and sat down in a state of shock.

'Tea or coffee Steve?' Julie said.

'Neither. Just a large brandy.'

'Don't worry, Steve – they're not back till tomorrow and we've still got unfinished business to attend to later.'

We all had a good laugh as we tucked into breakfast. Ann cuddled up to me and said, 'Would you like to come and watch my brother play football this morning? It's only up the road – it's the semi-final of the local cup.'

'Yeah, why not? We could all go.'

Within half an hour we were in Julie's Austin 1100 and heading for the football ground. It was the local senior amateur stadium, a really nice ground with a small stand. Ann introduced us to her younger brother, Neil. He looked a worried lad as he said, 'We've got a major problem. Four of our players are stuck on a train A second team player got married in Carlisle yesterday and four of our first team squad went to the wedding. They caught the first train out this morning but there's been a derailment so they can't get here and of course all the second team players are still at the wedding venue.'

'That ain't a problem,' said Steve. 'Nick and I will turn out for you if you can find us some boots.'

I looked at Steve and thought he'd gone mad.

Neil looked at us and said, 'Can you play?'

'We can play a bit,' I said.

'I'll go and get our manager so he can have a chat with you.'

Steve and I have played a good standard of football – as mentioned before, I had a few games for Ipswich youth team and Steve was on West Ham's books as a youngster a few years back.

In between playing in the band we turned out for Brentwood, who played in the Metropolitan League against teams like West Ham's A team and Wimbledon. We also graced the Athenian and Southern leagues, so we can do a bit. When we're not playing in the group we play for a local team. Both of us wanted to be professional footballers when we left school, but like many others we didn't have that little bit extra.

Within a couple of minutes Neil was back with the manager. Looking flustered and wearing an old Hull City tracksuit, the bloke, who was in his sixties, said, 'Neil tells me you've offered to play for us.'

'That's right,' said Steve.

'You can play, can't you? You're not a couple of southern softies?'

I nearly told him to piss off but, with the girls looking on, I kept my mouth shut. Steve jumped in – he could see my face and said, 'Yeah we've played a bit.'

'OK, there's no other option. We'll take a gamble with you. You need to sign a couple of forms first. Come with me and we'll sort some kit and boots out for you.'

Ann gave me a kiss on the cheek and said, 'That's nice of you to offer to play this game. It means the world to Neil – he's never reached a cup final before.'

Julie said to Steve sarcastically, 'You're not messing these lads about? You can play football?'

'Julie, do we look like a couple of shysters?'

The girls laughed and Julie replied, 'Yeah…'

We signed the forms and went into the dressing room with Neil, who introduced us to our new team mates. They didn't look too impressed, and as soon as we opened our mouths the captain, who was in his thirties, and built like a tank, said, 'You cockneys can play? You won't let us down? This team is in a league above us and we've never beat them. We need to play like our life depends on it to get any type of result.'

I was starting to lose my temper, and wished that Steve hadn't put our names in the frame. With a pounding headache through too much of everything last night, I felt like a sack of manure.

'We won't let you down,' said Steve, who looked worse than me.

The footwear they gave us looked like boots from the 1950s. Big brown bastards, so heavy I thought I was carrying an extra leg. We ran onto the pitch. I was surprised at how many people were watching – there must've been well over 100 spectators. I was asked to play right-half and Steve was up front. The other team looked like they'd just come out of Strangeways. This was going to be a Custer's last stand job. Within a couple of minutes I could see it was a kick-and-rush game – not much skill and certainly no finesse. Muck and bullets comes to mind. They had a very quick young winger who within a few minutes had put a ball on their centre forward's head and we were one-nil down. The team's heads dropped. I could see this winger causing havoc during the match; our full-back, who was marking him, was so slow a bottle of milk could turn quicker than him.

Steve said to me as he ran by, 'That winger has got to have few hard tackles to see what he's made of, Nick.'

This winger had the ball, and as he was coming towards me he tried to nutmeg me. I showed him the line and as he tried one of his tricks I tackled him hard but fair. I did that a couple of times and he drifted out of the game. He didn't want any more. He came off injured and had an early bath with the Palmolive. Steve and I were now on a mission and starting to enjoy ourselves. Steve took on their centre-half, beat him and passed the ball to Neil, who slotted it home. One-all at half-time, and our team mates became our best friends as they realised we could play.

Our manager was ecstatic and praised me and Steve. He gave his team talk, then we were out for the second half. Before I went out I puked up in the bog. I felt rough and I was knackered. Steve didn't look any better. In the second half, because I'd helped put their winger out of action, I was a marked man. I had to be careful as I'd got a tour to finish and didn't want to be crocked. With a few minutes to go their centre-half came towards me like an express train in their 18-yard box. As he tried to break my leg I shimmied to one side and fell over. The ref immediately gave a penalty. They went loopy-loo, and I just walked away as the ref booked some of their players. Steve picked up the ball and put it on the penalty spot. The bloke who normally took them looked well annoyed. Being a big-headed bastard, Steve couldn't help himself as he faced up to take it. The goalkeeper dived to his left and saved it. I couldn't believe it – he'd messed it up. Suddenly the ref blew his whistle and said it has to be retaken as the goalkeeper moved before the penalty was taken. So Steve put the ball back on the spot to retake it. He turned to us with a grin on his face and said, 'Don't worry, lads – it was only a practice shot.'

He ran up, buried the ball in the back of the net and went on a run, and we won the match two-one. Back in the dressing room Steve was a hero and I've never seen so many happy faces. Then it was into the bar with the girls and the players for a few pints of Hull Export. I noticed that Steve kept going to the bog, and said to him, 'Why do you keep going in the khazi?'

'I keep thinking about Julie's old man and what would happen if I got her pregnant, so I've topped up on johnnies from the machine.'

'You going for the world record in one-night bunk-ups?'

'I thought tonight I'll double up – I don't want to come unstuck.'

'What do you mean, double up?'

'Well, I'm going to put two on, or even three. I can't take any chances – he'd kill me.'

As we left, the manager and players thanked us. It felt great to be part of a winning team. We headed back to Julie's on a high. The girls were happy and so were we. With adrenalin pumping and a few pints under our belt, we had a passionate couple of hours. Afterwards Julie and Ann went into the kitchen and put some grub on. We opened some more bottles of wine that we'd bought on the way back, put the record player on and started playing Badfinger's *Come And Get It*. This was the life – it didn't get any better than this! An alluring girl, more passion later, a great win at football and the girls busying themselves making us a fry-up. Steve looked like Lord Muck in Julie's Dad's striped blue dressing gown.

We sat around the table having our food in a state of undress. I'd never felt so happy. This was the life of a pop star. Suddenly and without warning the front door opened and Julie's Mum and Dad were standing there. I don't know who was more shocked. Then it kicked off with her Dad, a brute of a man, who completely lost it and roared at Julie, 'What the hell is happening here, and why has that long-haired yob got my dressing gown on?'

After the initial shock Julie calmly said, 'Dad, meet Steve. He's in a well-known Essex band, Modern Edge. They're touring around Yorkshire and he's my steady.'

Steve looked at her as if to say, that's news to me. Like a donut, he got up and attempted to shake her Dad's hand. But the touch paper had been lit. Her Dad tried to get hold of Steve across the table, while Julie and her Mum were holding him back from clumping him. Then Julie's old man rushed upstairs like a madman, and her Mum said to Ann sarcastically, 'I thought you were a nice girl, Ann.'

'I am.'

'It doesn't look like that to me with all your underwear on show. Your mum would be very disappointed in you, Ann.'

'Look, Mrs Tadcastle, I know it looks bad and I'm sorry you've seen us like this, but I'm not ashamed of anything. Nick is also my steady. We're not children any more, we're adults, and we can make up our own minds what we want to do.'

I looked at Ann and thought how quickly she'd grown up. Not so long ago she wouldn't have said boo to a goose. I thought the girls were standing up to this really well until Julie's old man came racing back down the stairs with a face like thunder. Steve and I closed our eyes when we saw him holding six empty johnny wrappers. To say he exploded is an understatement – he was shaking like a lump of jelly as he spat out, 'Do you know, Joan, they've been sleeping in our bed, can you believe it, our daughter, the dirty little hussy, has been in our bed with that long-haired yob?' He waved the empty condom packets under his daughter's nose and said, 'What have you got to say about these, my girl?'

Julie was a hero in my eyes as she calmly said, 'Better to have protection, Dad. I don't want to get pregnant.'

I thought to myself that there was no chance of that happening with Steve 'doubling up'. The insults were fast and furious, even more so when Steve, with a glint in his eye, said to Julie's Dad, 'I love your daughter and you could be seeing a lot more of me. I'm sure you will get to like me when you know me better.'

Julie then got hold of Steve's hand to show their love. I couldn't believe what was happening. Her Dad finally lost it and threw a vase at Steve. It missed and smashed against a picture, which fell to the ground. Her mother started sobbing, but her Dad just stood there with the veins in his neck pulsating. He kept looking at the condom packets and shaking his head. The final crescendo was when he looked at Steve and me and said angrily, 'I'll have you two! You haven't heard the last of me! Julie – get dressed and stay out of my sight. The rest of you can disappear as well. You're a disgrace to the youth of today. Get out of my house!'

Within minutes we were heading to Ann's house in Julie's motor. I just couldn't believe how the girls were taking all of this; they seemed to have lost their inhibitions and were now on a different path of life. We went into the house, found out that her brother Neil was still celebrating the win at the local, and her parents had gone to church. Within minutes we were at it again, me upstairs with Ann and Steve and Julie on the sofa.

As I was going upstairs, Steve said under his breath, 'Got any johnnies?'

'Oh, leave it out, will yer? The way you're going through them I'm going to buy shares in Durex.'

The girls were up for it more than me and Steve were. After all the aggravation and Julie's father's threats about hearing from him again, it rather put us off, but not for long!

After about an hour Ann made us some cheese on toast and a cup of tea. I said to Julie, who strangely seemed very buoyant, 'Where does this leave you at home after all that's happened?'

'They'll get over it. I must admit it was a shock for all of us, but life moves on. In fact, Ann and I are thinking of moving down to London to live. I've got a brother who has done well for himself. He said we can have one of his flats to live in until we sort ourselves out.'

Ann grabbed my hand and said, 'Would you like to see more of me, Nick?'

'Of course I would – that'd be great.'

I gave her a kiss, and a bit of Cheddar stuck to her cheek. We all had a good laugh. What a day it had been, but it was back on the road tomorrow so we had to get back to our digs. Julie said she'd run us there, and she had the last laugh when she said to Steve, 'I forgot to tell you, I'm on the pill.'

Steve's face was a picture. 'Why didn't you tell me? I've spent a fortune on French letters!'

'Well, I didn't know where you'd been before. I didn't want to catch anything.'

Next morning we all turned up at the theatre on time – even Ronnie, looking bright-eyed and bushy-tailed. He wouldn't say, but looking at his happy mush he'd had a result – some poor bastard had been tucked up somewhere. The other band members also looked happy, so birds were definitely involved. We loaded up in the theatre's car park ready for the trip to Goole. We were playing at the local assembly hall, which, according to Terry and the Tanks, was a right old dive.

We'd just about finished when a police car entered the car park. We all looked alarmed as the two coppers got out of their Ford Anglia and marched over to us.

'Ronnie, what've you been up to?' asked Tone.

'Nothing! I'm clean!'

One of the coppers, a sergeant in his fifties, went straight over to Ronnie, who was wearing his long, black leather jacket and in the sergeant's eyes was suspicious.

'Who are you then, son?'

In a posh Essex accent, which was chronic, Ronnie replied, 'I'm the driver and roadie for the band Modern Edge. We're loading up for the drive to Goole, our next venue, officer.'

The sergeant raised his eyebrows and looked at the other copper, who was quite young.

'Is that so? Show me your driving licence.'

Ronnie got it out of his wallet and handed it to him. He scanned it with his beady eyes, looked up and said, 'Right, Donald…'

Steve started laughing and without thinking butted in, 'Feckin' Donald?'

The sergeant quickly turned and looked at Steve, growling,

'Isn't that his real name, then?'

Rick, quick as a flash, said, 'It's just that we call him Don. I mean, Donald's a right naff name, ain't it?'

The young copper, who was not happy, said, 'That's my name.'

The two coppers then frisked us down, I suppose they were looking for drugs. They then went through the bus with a fine-tooth comb. The bus, being nearly new, was perfect and they were getting more annoyed by the minute because they couldn't find anything to pin on us. As we left they just stood there. The sergeant spoke on his radio, then they left.

Going up the road, Ray looked at Ronnie, who was driving, and said, 'Do you know why they gave us a tug? And where's Donald come into this?'

'I ain't got a clue. You know I lost my licence.'

'No we didn't,' said an alarmed Steve.

'I got done for speeding, no tax and insurance twice, so they gave me a ban for a year. But it's all right – I got this moody licence under the name of Donald Cray, so it's all cool.'

We couldn't believe what we were hearing. Words failed us. We said no more until we got to the Goole gig. If there was ever a gig we didn't want to play it was this one. All of us were tired and ratty, mostly self-inflicted. The other band members had all had a good night at a party, so they felt like Steve and me. Only Ronnie was looking normal, which was a first. It was pouring down with rain, cold and the wind blew right through you. The dismal hall didn't help – what a dump! The caretaker, who looked like a thin crisp, took us through. As we walked in we disturbed a couple of bats, which flew over our heads and disappeared through a hole in the ceiling. What a fright! We were expecting to see Alfred Hitchcock appear. Ronnie could see we were arsey, so he said it might be better for us to go to our digs and get our heads down for a couple of hours while he set up.

We arrived at the digs in a back street that made Coronation Street look like the Ritz. The old girl with a roll-up hanging out of her mouth showed us our rooms – well, in fact one room. It was getting worse by the minute as we all slumped on these camp beds and closed our eyes, hoping that when we woke up we wouldn't be there.

After a good sleep we stopped off and got some fish and chips. Ronnie had been a diamond and everything was set up perfectly. Even the set lists were laid out. As Tone went behind his drum kit I had a funny feeling that he was up to his old tricks with drugs. When the copper checked him over he'd gone pale. He'd had a pork pie hat on but the young copper had never looked inside it. He'd looked relieved as nothing was found.

Steve came over to me and whispered in my ear, 'Do you think that check was random or do you think Julie's Dad is on our case?'

'The latter, and I don't think we've seen the last of them.'

I pulled Ronnie aside and had a quiet word. 'Are there any more surprises coming our way?'

'No, you're OK, Nick. Its only the licence and insurance that's naughty.'

'Why don't I believe you, Ronnie? Have you got any skulduggery going on with the local villains?'

'No – it's a bit of a holiday for me. I'm going straight, Nick.'

'Oh, feck off, Ronnie, you couldn't walk a straight line if you tried, and what about the dodgy name, Cray, on that moody licence. That was a bit close to the real thing.'

He gave a wide grin, winked and said, 'Did you like that?'

I was missing Ann and I gave her a bell. She wanted to know when I'd see her again. I was hoping to see her before we went back down South. She told me that Julie's parents were giving her a hard time. They'd come back early because her mother had a bad migraine. After that, the headache must've gone into mega-mode.

It was nearly a full hall and we got stuck into the two sets. I must admit I've heard us play better, but we did what we were paid for. After the show Steve and I went back to haunted towers for an early night. The others went out to sample the night life in Goole – so they'd probably be home early!

Next day we were off to Bridlington. When we arrived at the Roxy for the show the manageress said that two people had been on the phone for me; one was Pauline at the office and somebody called Eric. I rang Pauline first and listened to her saying how much she missed me, which took about 2 seconds, then about her new bloke. Meeting all these pop stars in the agency, me not being one of them, she'd now been pulled by a very well-known lead guitarist. He was good looking, had two records with his band in the Top 10 and one in America. With a brand new BMW and a flat overlooking the Thames in Cheyne Walk, Chelsea, it was no contest. I was not bitter as I recalled the previous night's abode and the fry-up in the morning, which had been so greasy I thought I was swallowing a pint of Castrol.

I didn't take a lot of notice of what she was saying until she said, 'Nick, I know you're not listening to what I'm saying but I think you will listen to this. A top Canadian group is over here in a few weeks for a short tour that TJ is promoting. The support band has cried off and you've got the gig.'

It didn't register at first as I was still bringing up bile from my breakfast. When she told me the name of the band I couldn't believe it. They were huge, so the question had to be asked.

'Why us Pauline? We're second-rate to them – in fact, fourth-rate.'

'They heard your song *Suburban Mod* in New York; it was on a radio station playing British records. Their management arm in London came to one of your gigs and were impressed. You do realise this is huge for the band? We're talking 6,000-plus audiences. When you get back from the Yorkshire tour, TJ wants to see you straight away to finalise everything.'

I went and told the lads, and they were blown away. What an opportunity for global recognition at last! An enormous stage with well-known stars – it didn't get any better than that! I nearly forgot to ring Eric, whoever he was, in all of the excitement.

It turned out that Eric was the manager of the football team we'd played for on the Sunday. I was very surprised at what he had to say. He wanted Steve and me to play for them this coming Sunday in the final, which I thought was a bit unfair to the blokes who had played all season. I said I would call back later after I'd had a word with Steve. We were playing Beverley on the Saturday night and Sunday was free. To see Ann and Julie again would be great. It didn't take long to say yes, so it was arranged that we'd meet up with them at the same ground on Sunday morning. I rang Ann, and she was over the moon that we were coming back so soon. She said I could kip down at her place on Sunday night. I didn't think Steve would get the same invite from Julie to stay at her place! In the meantime, after all that excitement we had a gig to play that night.

We had a couple of hours to kill so Steve and I had a brisk walk along the prom. We lit up our Park Drive cigarettes and looked out at the sea. It was nice to relax and take on board what had happened over the past few weeks. Our love lives were back on track and, with a nationwide tour to look forward to, life was sweet. But our peace and quiet were shattered when we heard a commotion coming from the left of us in the distance. Some pricks on pedal cars! As they got nearer the pricks turned out to be Ray, Rick, Tone and Ronnie, racing along the prom Formula 1 style. People were jumping out of the way as they went hell for leather. Then the inevitable happened when Rick lost control, hit Ray's car on the downward slope, and went over the edge and into the sea. We hauled him out and just couldn't stop laughing as he stood there looking like a drowned rat.

We got back to the hall ready for the gig and the laughter stopped. Tone and Rick had a right bust-up. Rick said to Tone, 'What did you just put in your mouth?'

'I've got a headache – it's only an aspirin.'

'I've never seen a blue aspirin before.'

'Oh bollocks – what are you, my keeper?'

Tone stormed off all stroppy like, only coming back a few minutes before the show. Nothing more was said but the writing was on the wall. Could he be back on drugs? The show and the other gigs for the week were OK. The only downside was that we got stopped by the police twice. They were definitely looking for something. Steve and I couldn't make up our mind whether it was Julie's old man giving us grief, or Ronnie mixing with local villains. On a couple of occasions he'd met up with some more dodgy-looking blokes. Another thought was that Tone was mixing with some drug dealers. He'd disappeared one night after a show and didn't come back till the next morning.

On the day of the football match, Steve and I had bought some football boots and were looking forward to the game. The others, including Ronnie, decided to come and give us a bit of moral support. Steve and I took the Cortina as we were going to stay the night.

We met up with Ann and Julie at the stadium for the afternoon kick-off. After the game they'd be having our undivided attention till Monday morning. Walking into the dressing room the players treated us like old friends. Eric gave his team talk and we walked on to the pitch for the final of the cup. There were about 300 spectators. The other team hadn't been beaten all season and were odds-on to win the game. Eric warned us that their match-winner was an ex-pro with Huddersfield Town. Even though he was in his late thirties, this centre-forward was mustard. We looked over at the other band members and the girls, and they gave us the thumbs-up.

Within a few minutes I could see that the other team were great on the ball, and they looked a different class to us. Their centre-forward was an animal, a nasty piece of work. They just kept sending high balls into our 18-yard box for him to run on to. As he won the ball he would use his elbows, go over the top on tackles and just bully his way through. He collided with our goalkeeper and took him out. The ref didn't want to know. Fortunately our keeper recovered, but had a nasty cut above his eye. Our team were mostly young lads and unfortunately didn't have the bottle to combat this. We went into half-time two-nil down courtesy of the animal. Heads were down and Eric tried to bring them up in his team talk.

I couldn't help myself and put my oar in, 'Eric, do you mind if I say a few words?'

'Go, ahead, Nick, if you think it can help.'

I raised my voice and scanned each player as I was talking.

'Look, lads, this might be the only chance you ever have in your football career to win a medal. You're going to have to get stuck in. You're being bullied – they think they've won already. They only have a plan A, which is to get the ball to the animal. Leave it to me. I'll take care of him in the first 10 minutes. Without being big-headed, Steve and I have played at a much higher level and have come up against this type of player before. His only interest is to hurt people. Now let's get out there and do the business and put the cup in your clubhouse.'

It appeared that my inspiring speech had fallen on deaf ears when our young full-back, who was only 17, failed to tackle the animal and he very nearly made it three-nil. With his half-hearted tackle the animal deliberately trod on his foot and he limped off to be replaced by our sub. It was payback time when, a few minutes later, he was running with the ball and I put in a sliding tackle full on. As he fell to the ground he wrenched his right knee. He was writhing about in agony and crying like a baby and was stretchered off, not to be seen again. I got booked and one or two of their players promised retribution, which never happened.

This was the start for us to move up a gear. With their main man on the way to hospital, the saying 'Live by the sword, die by the sword' came to mind. As I suspected, they didn't have a plan B and we got on top of them.

Steve scored with a bullet-like header and we were all over them. With 10 minutes to go our right-winger run past their full back and planted the ball in the back of the net. It was two-all and with the final kick of normal time Ann's brother Neil got between two defenders and toe-poked the ball into the net from a Steve free kick. It was pandemonium as the ref blew the final whistle. Eric and the players were jumping for joy. Eric had been part of this club for more than 30 years. Steve and I felt proud that we had done our bit for the club as we were presented with our winner's medals and, of course, the treasured cup.

With Ann by my side, we all headed off to a local working men's club. The football club had booked it for the night so it was party time. The band and Ronnie were now part of the club's family as everybody celebrated. What a party it was! Unfortunately, there's always a wanker who wants to spoil it for everybody else. The club captain, Alan, was at the bar getting in some drinks, and two blokes in their late twenties, who should have known better, were getting a bit lairy and one of them said loudly to Alan, 'Who's this divvy, then?'

A young Down's syndrome lad of about 12 was by Alan's side. 'He's my brother, and don't you dare call him that.'

Ronnie was by the bar and heard what the bloke had said. He

put his drink down, went up to Alan and said, 'Take your brother into the bog for a moment.'

Once they had left the bar, Ronnie said to this idiot, 'That wasn't very nice what you just said about that young lad, was it?'

The bloke responded, 'What's that got to do with you? Get back to London before you get hurt.'

The room went quiet and the bloke went up close to Ronnie in a threatening manner. Quick as a flash Ronnie hit him, and he collapsed like a pack of cards. Ronnie said to his mate, 'Get this scumbag out of here before I put one on you as well.'

He dragged his mate, who was all over the shop, out of the club. Everybody was shocked, and the club steward said to Ronnie, 'I don't know who you are, lad, but the drinks are on me for you all night. That bloke, Jake, has finally got his just desserts. He's a nasty piece of work – everybody hates him.'

Little did anyone know that Ronnie had a Down's syndrome brother who he thought the world of. Within a couple of minutes the party was back on and a local group got ready to play on the stage. The band was having a great time and the locals made us welcome, especially a couple of girls who made a beeline for Rick and Ray. Tone kept disappearing outside every now and again so he was back on the weed, but tonight it was chill-out time. Steve said that after the party Julie and him were going to sneak into Julie's parent's summer house at the bottom of the garden for the night. She'd said to her parents that she was sleeping round Ann's, so he was sorted. Mind you, rather him than me. It was getting really frosty outside – hopefully he wouldn't freeze his nuts off.

The band started up and they weren't bad, but the inevitable happened when we were asked to play a few numbers. By this time we were well oiled but did manage to play a couple: *All Right Now* by Free, *Lola* by the Kinks and *Reflections of my Life* by Marmalade. Even Ronnie sang a couple of numbers, which weren't bad. It was a day to remember and we made a lot of new friends. The party was still full on as we left for Ann's, which was walking distance away. Steve and Julie had already left for a night in the summer house.

We crept into Ann's house, but her parents never went to sleep until their offspring were home, so as soon as the key went into the door a voice from upstairs said, 'Is that you, Ann?' 'Yes, Mum. And before you ask, Neil is staying round his mates tonight so you can go to sleep. We're just having a cup of coffee, so good night.'

Her Mum wouldn't let it rest. 'I've made up the bed in the box room for Nick.'

'Thanks Mum! Good night.'

We gave the coffee a miss and had a snog and a hands-of-the-desert moment till we thought her parents were asleep. After about half an hour we crept upstairs into Ann's room and listened. We could hear gentle snoring in the master bedroom, so it was the green light. Unfortunately we got carried away and the headboard took a bit of a hammering. Ann started giggling and said, 'Shush! You'll wake Mum and Dad up.'

Which we had, and we heard her mother say to her husband, 'Albert, you have shut our bedroom window, haven't you? I can hear a woodpecker attacking one of our apple trees again.'

Our last gig of the tour was at Whitby, renowned for its fishing fleet. It had been a memorable trip and we were in good spirits as we played the last gig in the Cellar club. Again we'd been stopped by the police on the last part of the tour, which was becoming an unhealthy occurrence. Ronnie was looking very shifty and a couple of blokes who he'd met before turned up. He was up to something.

We set up, then had the best fish and chips ever down by the harbour. Then it was down to business as we started the first set. As it was the last show we played some of our own new material that was going to be part of our two short sets on tour with the Canadians. It seemed to go down well. Normally after the gig we'd shoot straight home, but Ronnie said, for whatever reason, that he wanted to stay overnight. Luckily some girls said there was a party on and we were all invited. That sealed it.

It was a great party. Plenty of everything, no hassle, plenty of girls, topped up with vast amounts of alcohol. I met a nice little girl, Sara, who could dance a mean twist and was full of fun. As I was having a nice smooch with her to the background of *Go Now* by the Moody Blues, she whispered in my ear, 'You have to kiss a lot of frogs before you meet a prince.'

I'd never heard that saying before so I said, 'Am I that prince?'

As she sent her tongue down my throat like a skier on a giant slalom, she said, 'No, but you'll do for me tonight.'

We fell out of the party about 6 in the morning, found a cafe and filled up on copious amounts of bacon, eggs, black pudding and the rest of a full English, washed down with mugs of Cecil Gee. When we went back to the Cellar club to load up for the long journey home. Ronnie was already stacking up the amps in the back of the bus. He seemed to be on charge as he was working full-out. As Steve was putting the mic stands into the back of the bus he was well surprised at what he saw. He pointed it out to the rest of the guys. It was a Wem base amp, a very big one that looked in good nick. He commented, 'Ronnie, we seem to have gained another amp on our travels.'

With sweat pouring off his face and looking like he'd been found with his hand in the till, he said, 'It's a surprise for yer. I saw it in a second-hand shop and it was a steal. It needs a bit of work on it but it'll do you a turn.'

'Is steal the operative word, Ronnie?' Rick said.

'This is ridgey-didge! Would I tell you a porky?'

'Yes', we all said.

'Right, let's load up and be on our toes,' said Ronnie, still looking guilty.

We loaded up and Ronnie said he would like to drive the Cortina for a change, with Tone riding shotgun. Ray drove the bus, with me next to him in case he fell asleep, and the rest sprawled out in various parts of the bus trying to get some shut-eye. After about half an hour two police cars in tandem pulled us over. The Cortina with the other two in shot by us like bats out of hell. I got out of the bus as the four policemen, one an inspector who looked liked he should've retired, said, 'What are you up to then, lads?'

I'd had enough of being stopped and I didn't hold back. 'Look, officer, we're a band that's been touring Yorkshire. Since we met two girls, one being Julie Tadcastle, whose father is probably your boss, we've been hassled and stopped six times. Now, call it coincidence but I reckon he's put the word out on us. He wants to find a way of charging us with something to get back at one of the band members for having a dabble with his daughter. Does that ring-a-ding-ding?'

I've never seen policemen lost for words before – they were gobsmacked. I knew there was going to be a price to pay, and it could go either way. Two of the young policemen were smirking, but the inspector wasn't. He was livid because he knew he'd been sussed.

'I don't know what you're talking about, lad. We're more interested in what you've got in the bus. Coming from Whitby we know one or two fishing boats come in with contraband. Drugs are another problem and you being a rock band, how do we know you're not carrying or using drugs?'

He then barked out an order that made the other coppers jump to attention.

'Get these long-haired yobs out of the bus and check them all over. Pull out the gear in the back of the vehicle so we can have a good look.'

'How do you know we've come from Whitby?'

'Because you look and smell fishy.'

I have to say I did have a grin when he said that, but I was now putting two and two together. That no-good Ronnie, no wonder he went past like a torpedo. I bet that Wem amp has something to do with it. Thank God Tone wasn't there, as I'm sure there'd be drugs on him. The others had the same thoughts as me, with all eyes on the amp at the back of the bus. The coppers weren't very gentle with the equipment and Steve tore into them.

'Will you be careful with our gear? It's worth a lot of money and it's our living!'

Everything was out except the Wem. Two of the coppers tried to pull it out but they were having difficulty. Now, it's heavy but it ain't that heavy.

Steve said, 'Be careful with that amp – it's worth a fortune. If you damage it we'll be claiming.'

The inspector said to us, all snide like, 'Why is it so heavy?'

Rick butted in and said politely, 'The reason is, it has four large speakers and it's made of solid wood. It's one of the biggest bass amps you can buy. All the top groups like the Stones and the Who use them. Now, if you want us to pull it out we're only too happy to do so, sir.'

We looked at the inspector, hoping he would say no, but he didn't.

'Yeah, pull it out.'

Rick and me went to the back and made a song and dance of trying to pull it out, hoping he would say don't bother. As soon as we got hold of it we knew there was some swag in there. Sweat was pouring from us as we moved it to the end of the bus.

The inspector was grinning. 'That's probably the hardest work you've ever done in your life. Now you can put it back and sweat some more.'

We didn't see Ronnie until we arrived back at Steve's to unload the gear. I was impressed with Rick that he knew the Stones and the Who had Wem amps until he told us it was a Hans Christian Andersen story.

We turned up and went to the back of Steve's house to put the gear into his garage. Waiting for us was Ronnie, looking as happy as a sandboy. I jumped out of the bus and let him have it.

'You tosser! What've you got in that speaker? You nearly got us all arrested!'

'Sorry about that, lads. I have a little present for you. Let's unload the bounty.'

We unloaded the bass amp and put it on the floor. Ronnie took a screwdriver out and undid the back of it. Our eyes were like saucers as we looked in. We couldn't believe it – more watches than Timex's warehouse, hundreds of them! Ronnie fished out one for each of us, screwed the back on the amp, put it back in the bus and shot off. Unbelievable!

♫ 14 ♫

The comeback

As soon as we got back, the band went to see Des, who was about a couple of weeks from getting out and about again. It was great to see him looking well again, and after the Ronnie experience we couldn't wait to have him back in the fold.

There were a few things to sort out. The first was with TJ regarding the mini-tour with the main-line band. By then we knew that Tone was back on drugs and decisions had to be made about him. Also, Steve and I had been thinking about a comeback against Anita and Jenny's boyfriends, Simon and Rupert. We didn't like what they did and I had an idea of how to get them back after reading an article in a national newspaper, but I needed to make a phone call first to Shelly, who managed the salon.

'Hi, Shelly, it's Nick from the band. Can you talk?'

'Yeah, no problem. Anita and Jenny are out. It's great to hear from you. You ringing me up to ask me out?'

'I thought you were courting strong.'

'I was, but I was getting bogged down. He wanted to get engaged and I didn't. I'm too young. I need to live a bit more before I settle down.'

I thought I could kill two birds with one stone here. 'When are you free?'

'I'm off for a few days starting tomorrow. I need to get out of Reading and see some fresh scenery. I've got my own car so I'm as free as a bird. In fact, I was going to Brentwood to see my sister. Is that anywhere near you?'

This was getting better and better,

'As it happens, not that far. Look, I know it's on the hoof, but why don't you come over to my place tomorrow. I've got some time off as well – we could go out and have some fun together.'

'Can't wait. Now, what was the real reason you rang me?'

'I need Simon and Rupert's home phone numbers and their

parents' numbers. Could you get them for me? And don't ask why.'

'Yeah, I can do that for you. I don't like the arrogant pigs, so it'll be a pleasure. I'll bring them with me tomorrow.'

I gave her my address, and she said she'd be at my place about lunchtime. I couldn't wait!

Steve and I went to see TJ about the tour. As we had a few days off, Rick, and Ray did their own thing while Tone said he was going up country to meet his sister, Penny, and her son, Robin. We still wondered who the father was – I was just hoping he didn't play lead guitar when he was older!

We walked into TJ's office after noticing his new Rolls-Royce Phantom VI, which was outside. We saw Pauline first. She looked well tasty, wearing a long white dress with a target sign on the front and a red leather beret.

'Is it raining in here? You've got your hat on.'

I must have caught her on her once-a-month moment, as she turned and said, 'Looking at you and Steve, it's about time you tidied yourselves up a bit. You're about three fashions behind everybody else. I know you played Oxford a few weeks ago – you must've gone into that new Oxfam shop down there.'

'Don't get cheeky, Pauline, just because you've got a flash boyfriend in a famous band. Just remember where you come from and how you got here. Perhaps you had a little bit of help on the way, eh?'

'He's not flash – he's really nice. In fact, I'm flying to Paris with him in the band's new plane for a gig at a big stadium in Paris tomorrow.'

'Is that right? You haven't heard about the strike by the French air traffic controllers tomorrow, then?'

'What!'

TJ came bounding out of his office full of the joys of spring.

'Come in, lads, come in. By the way, how's Des getting on?'

'Nice of you to ask. He's on the road to recovery,' I said.

Since the last time we'd been in his office it had certainly changed. There were leather chairs, furniture that wasn't from MFI, and photos of famous bands adorned the walls. And a Rolls parked outside. He was now moving in the fast lane.

'See all these bands? I've booked them all. I'm now one of the top agents and promoters in the country.'

'I'm well pleased for you,' said Steve. 'Oh, by the way, any news on our new recording contract?'

He changed the subject immediately and went back into business mode. Now, with him you have to appear not to be that excited about what he does for you. He will see that as a weakness and you won't get the going rate even though you're jumping for joy inside.

'Terrific news about you lot going on tour with these stars. I had to pull out all the stops for this one – they wanted a Top 10 British band as a support act.'

'So you wasn't having us on about them hearing our record on a New York radio station,' I said.

'That's kosher! How lucky you are to have me in your corner sorting this fantastic booking for you.'

'What's the catch?' said Steve.

'What're you on about, a catch? You don't know how lucky you are.'

It was now time to get excited as I said warmly, 'Yeah, top booking, TJ! What's the SP, then?'

'That's better! Show a bit of gratitude to your No 1 fan.'

We all started laughing and Steve said, 'Oh, leave it out! We've earned you plenty of money over the years.'

Pauline walked in with a tray of coffees and bickies, and plonked it down on the table, giving me the evil eye.

'And what about Pauline?' I said. 'What an asset she's been to you. You've got me to thank for that.'

'Don't you know when to give up, Nick?' she said.

The door slammed and one of the pictures came off the wall. TJ quickly got off his arse and put the Zombies back up.

'What's wrong with you two? Right, back to business. It's only seven dates: London, Glasgow, Newcastle, Manchester, Cardiff, Bristol and back to London. You'll be doing two short 15-minute sets, one each half. This is big time, prodigious venues and large crowds. You've got to be at your very best. It starts in ten days' time. Everything is laid on – all you have to do is play. I've booked up Elm Park again to practise for a couple of days, then two days before the tour begins we do a dress rehearsal with the other band.'

'The wages will reflect this star booking?' Steve said.

'Christ, bands would do this for nothing. We'll talk about that later. We need to agree what numbers you'll be playing.' He handed over a folder to me. 'Everything you need to know is in there. Oh, by the way, how's Tony? He's not back on the aspirin is he?'

'No, he's fine,' I said.

I quickly got off the subject and we said our goodbyes. Once we got out of the office we jumped for joy – what a result! Couldn't wait! We headed back to Romford and Monty's cafe as I now wanted to put my plan together to deal with them jods Simon and Rupert. We met Des and the three of us walked into the cafe. The glare and sparkle of new watches on show was blinding!

As Monty clapped eyes on us he said, 'Here they come – the Beverley Sisters. Hope you're hungry, lads – you've got to try my new sausages.'

'I think I'll give it a miss, Monty. Last time I had your new sausages I went up the road mumbling ee-haw ee-haw and kicking out at everybody.'

'What do you want then?'

'Steak and kidney pie, chips and beans three times.'

We found a table and I said to Monty, 'Have you seen Willy about?'

'Probably in the bookies, or should be here in about an hour's time.'

'What're you up to, Nick?' asked Steve.

'I was reading a sports page and I noticed that an England B rugby team is playing Scotland B this Saturday.'

'So what? You don't like rugby.'

'I know that, Steve, just listen. We know Simon and Rupert play rugby at county level. I know it's a long shot, but what I'm thinking is that somebody rings them up saying they're one of the England B selectors. The spiel is that a sickness bug has brought down some of the team and we need replacements and you have both been selected if you're available. We'd do this about 4pm on the Friday. What do you think, lads?'

'That would be one big con if you could pull it off,' says Des.

'Fantasy world comes to mind, Nick,' Steve said.

'We know Willy is a top con man and when he wants to he can put on a cut-glass accent that would fool anybody. I've spoken to Shelly at the salon and she is getting me their phone numbers – she's bringing them down to me tomorrow.'

'What do you mean, coming down tomorrow?'

'Didn't I tell you, Steve? She's spending a couple of days with me.'

'You've kept that quiet.'

Just then Willy walked in, in his forties, weasel-like features and skinny as a rake. I shouted over to him, 'Willy – got a minute?'

He sat down with us and I said, 'Do you want a sausage sarnie?'

'You're joking! I had one here yesterday. I was up all night with the trots.'

The girl brought over our steak and kidney pies and Willy said, 'I'll have one of those and a cup of Rosie. Now, what do you want, young Nick?'

I outlined my plan and Willy was impressed. 'So, what do you want me to do?'

'I want you to use your cut-glass accent to take off the England team selector.'

'What, like this?' The transformation of a cockney accent into a posh Chelsea accent was brilliant. 'You give me the script, and I'll do it for you. But what's in it for me?'

'I'll give you a good drink and I've got a nice watch for you.'

'Not one of Ronnie's watches? The whole of Romford was late for work this morning.'

We all had a good laugh and I came up with an amount he was happy with. I gave him my address and his drink money up front and it was all systems go.

The next day I had a dust and hoover round ready for the arrival of Shelly. I'd known her for quite a long time because of her working in Anita's salon. Once or twice I nearly dated her, but she was too frightened because she was worried about losing her job. Now that was out of the window we were free of any ties, so hopefully we'd have a couple of days together. She was slightly younger than me, dark eyes, long black hair and olive-skinned, a real head-turner. I made sure I put on an extra splash of Old Spice.

She turned up in her white Hillman Imp. I hadn't seen her for a few months but she looked just as lovely. We gave each other a cuddle and I made her a cup of coffee and a sandwich.

'Great to see you, Nick.'

'Likewise. You look great. Good journey down?'

'Yeah. I hear you're going on tour with the Canadians soon. We've already got tickets for the Bristol gig. The whole salon's coming, and before you ask Anita is not one of them.'

After some more small talk Shelly laughed and said, 'What's all this about wanting the poison dwarves' phone numbers?'

'"Poison dwarves"? What's that all about, Shelly?'

'They're so arrogant and full of themselves, nobody likes them. I don't know why Anita and Jenny go out with them.'

'Well, you might like this. Ever since the two of them and their mates threw us out of the pub for no reason, Steve and I have wanted to get even. Now, listen to this.'

I told her about the rugby match in Scotland and how we were going to try and set them up. 'What do you think?'

'If you can pull it off it'll be brilliant, Nick! I've got the numbers you want. Anita and Jenny leave their diaries about in the salon so it was quite simple to get them.'

'Somehow we've got to contact them between 4 and 5 tomorrow. Any thoughts?'

'You might be lucky because every Friday about 5 o'clock they come and pick up Anita and Jenny and go for drinks at a posh club in town.'

'Brilliant! Do you know what rugby club they play for and maybe the name of one of their managers or coaches?'

'The main man at their rugby club comes into the salon. I have his phone number in my appointments book, which I always carry about with me. Hold on – it's in the car.'

The rest of the day and night I spent with Shelly. It was what we both needed, no more to be said.

Then Friday afternoon was upon us and there was an air of

excitement to see whether we could pull it off. Willy was on time
and I had the script all ready. With Steve and Des looking on, we
were ready to go. The first calls were to their home numbers, with
no answer, as we expected. Then on to their parents, but again
nobody was in. The third call was to the main man at the rugby
club; he was out, but we left a message with his wife. This wasn't
looking too good, and as he made the last call to the salon we were
all holding our breath. Willy was as cool as a cucumber – this was
just another day in the office for him.

Willy got through and said, 'Hello, I'm sorry to trouble you I'm
trying to contact Simon Chandler. He is? Could I have a word
with him, please? Hello, Simon, this is Douglas Grainger. We have
met before at a county game you were playing at. The reason for
the call is that I'm one of the selectors of the England B rugby
team. You're aware that we are playing Scotland B tomorrow
afternoon at Murrayfield. Unfortunately we have had a sickness
bug that has decimated the team and that's why I'm calling you.
We would like you to join up with the team as a matter of urgency.
It is too late to get a flight for Edinburgh, so unfortunately it's a
journey by car, not an ideal preparation for a game that you will
play in… I'm very serious! I have been chasing you all afternoon
and have left a message with your club chairman Tony Riley's wife
for you to contact me. Now, are you available, Simon, as I have
others to contact? I can assure you I am Douglas Grainger and
you will be playing, but look, if you are not sure about playing for
your country, I need to know now… Fine, that is great news. You
might be able to help me. I'm trying to contact one of your county
colleagues, Rupert Darcy… Rupert is there? Can I have a word
with him, please?'

Willy did the same spiel with Rupert and said to him, 'If you
can both report to the Royal Kirk Hotel in Kirknewton, which is
not far from Edinburgh, and the England boys will welcome you…
You want my phone number just in case? No problem – it is 01708
4395, and I'm Douglas Grainger. The number I have given you is
the South East regional rugby headquarters. I'm here for another
hour. I'll look forward to meeting you both on your England
debuts.'

'That was magic, Willy. You're a top man!' I said.

'Don't count your chickens just yet. I reckon we're going to get a phone call,' said Steve.

'You're going to have to answer it, Shelly, and say South East regional rugby headquarters, then pass it over to Willy – or Douglas Grainger,' I said.

'What if they recognise my voice?'

'No, they won't. Just talk like you've got a plum in your mouth, or something else.'

Everybody looked at me in amazement and went into hysterics.

'What have I said wrong? What's so funny?'

Then I twigged it, but suddenly the phone rang. I said to Shelly, 'You're on,' and she gingerly picked the phone up and said confidently, 'Good afternoon, South East regional rugby headquarters. How can I help you?' She listened, then said, 'I think you have the wrong number.'

In a panic I said, 'Who was that?'

'Somebody for you. She sounded common and well rough.'

Under my breath I thought, 'Mandy's back in town'. Then the phone rang again.

Shelly said the good afternoon bit, looked over to Willy and said, 'I'll put you through to Mr Grainger now.'

Willy took the phone and went straight in. 'Douglas Grainger speaking... Hello, Simon.' He listened for a short while, then said, 'Of course, I would do the same thing. Look forward to seeing you in Scotland and hopefully a win for us. All the best.'

'Has he sussed it out, Willy?' I said.

'No, he just wanted to make sure it was all above board. Only time will tell if he's taken the bait.'

'How will we know that?'

Shelly butted in and said, 'I'll give Anita a ring in an hour on some other pretext.'

It was a long wait until Shelly spoke to Anita. 'Have you missed me? How was business this week?' Shelly listened to the reply, then said, 'Doing much over the weekend?'

I could see by Shelly's smiling face that the bait had been taken. Another couple of minutes on the phone and the call finished.

'Just to let you know that the poison dwarves are on their way to bonnie Scotland.'

We all jumped up in the air in delight and I said with the biggest smile I could muster, 'Let's get down the Queen's for a pint or two.'

'Willy, you're a star!' I said.

Shelly went up to the bedroom to freshen up.

Des said, 'It's a feckin' long way to Jock-land on the A1 in the pouring rain, especially at night.'

'I'd give a month's money to see their faces when they arrive at the Royal Kirk Hotel. It's only a glorified bed and breakfast. I got it out of my Dad's old AA book. I knew it would come in handy one day.'

Shelly stayed more than two days; in fact, she never did see her sister in Brentwood. We had a great time together and it was a chill-out time for both of us. A bit of sea air at Maldon, Southend and Clacton was just what we needed. With all the touring you just don't have any time to enjoy some free down time. Shelly agreed not to tell anyone in the salon where she'd been. We said our goodbyes, which lasted all day. I said I would bell her nearer the time to make arrangements to see her after the show in Bristol.

Why is it always the drummer?

We'd all had a great few days. Tone was late coming back from his sister's, and alarm bells started to ring. We had rehearsals at Elm Park in a couple of days' time ready for the journey of a lifetime with this star band. TJ kept ringing me up like an old fanny to make sure we were focused for the tour – he was getting a right pain in the arse. Then a bombshell dropped when I answered the phone.

'Hello, Nick. It's Penny. How are you?'

I automatically thought she was going to tell me who the father of her child was, and was hoping it wasn't me.

'Hi, Penny, nice to hear from you. You and baby Robin well?'

'Yeah, everything is fine my end, but I'm afraid all is not well with Tony. I don't know if you are aware but he's had a relapse with the demons again. A couple of nights ago he met up with some of his old druggie friends and overdosed on cocaine and nearly died. So he won't be coming back to the band in the near future. Mum and Dad are booking him into a place in North Wales where they cater for drug abuse. They're paying for this out of their own pocket to try and help him.'

'I'm so sorry Penny. Please give him our best and we'll be thinking about him.'

'I will. If I didn't have Robin I'd help you out for a few weeks until you get a replacement. I know you've got this prestige tour coming up.'

'That's nice of you, Penny. Thanks for letting us know, and please keep us informed about Tone's progress.'

As I put the phone down I had mixed emotions. Tone and I had been mates ever since we were at school together. I felt really sorry for him and his parents, who I knew well, just working-class people who were now trying to save their son from destroying himself. They were one of many thousands of parents across the country doing the same thing with their children. Then panic set in and maybe selfishness – what about the tour only a few days away? Within a couple of hours the others were round my house and I told them the news. Of course they were as sad as me that his addiction had finally caught up with him again. We agreed that we would put in some money between us and send it to his Mum and Dad to help with the costs. Des, being Des, took a wad of cash out of his wallet and bunged it in the pot. Then it was down to business.

'Anyone know a drummer?' I asked.

'I spoke to Billy last week but he's still happy in Suffolk,' said Ray.

'I heard Dinky's drummer and bass guitarist left last week,' said Rick.

'Well, we have their bass player, and he's mustard!' piped up Ray.

'Oh, piss off, Ray – there's nobody better than me,' said an angry Steve.

'What about the fall-out with TJ? He's going to go ballistic,' said Des.

Nobody had any answers, so I said I'd meet them at the pub later after I'd had a word with Terry. He'd always got his ear to the ground. The boys left except Steve and Des. We couldn't wait to ring Shelly to see what had happened with the poison dwarves. The news was brilliant; she said they'd arrived at the bed and breakfast after a hellish 8-hour journey. They were not impressed – they couldn't understand why an England team would stay at a dump like that. Nor was the landlady, who they woke up at 3 in morning. Her husband threatened them with violence and told them to sling their hooks. To say they were upset was an understatement! When Anita and Jenny told the girls in the salon they couldn't stop laughing, which didn't impress them. Within a few hours their escapade had got back to the rugby club and they had the piss taken out them unmercifully. Now their main aim in life was to find the culprits. I was lucky – they couldn't have kept the phone number I'd given them, otherwise I would've heard by now.

I rang Terry from the Tanks and told him our problem. He said he'd ring me back in an hour to see if anybody was available. When he rang back I was surprised by what he said. He said he would drum for us. As mentioned before, he was one of those blokes who could play anything. He had a few gigs already booked with the Tanks, but his brother Gerry was going to fill in for him so he was available. This was good news, because he had a good voice and he would help with back-up vocals. So, subject to the others agreeing to it, it was a done deal. Over a drink at the Queen's the others quickly agreed that this was good news.

At the Elm Park rehearsals Terry got plenty of stick, with him looking like Hank Marvin. We agreed the numbers we were going to play, all of it our own material. The time we had on stage worked out to about eight numbers in total. Terry fitted in well and he canned the numbers pretty quickly. After two full days of practising we felt that we were ready to go.

Now there was just one last hurdle, which was TJ. He would not be happy about a change of drummer just before a high-profile tour, and I could fully understand that. All along he hadn't wanted Tone to return to the band, so we'd get plenty of verbal from him. We'd tell him at the last moment – we didn't want him to have a heart attack on the biggest show he'd ever promoted.

A few days later we were at the theatre for a full dress rehearsal. To say we were nervous was an understatement. As we walked in with our guitars we were met by the tour manager, Jimbo, a guy in his forties who, I gather, was one of the best in his field. It was a busy scene as everybody was setting up. It appeared that the main act hadn't arrived yet. The band was a four-piece including an English bass player. Their music was somewhere between the Byrds and the Lovin' Spoonful. I gather they were a handful to control, so Jimbo was going to be busy. TJ still didn't know about Terry, but that was all going to change as he walked in, closely followed by Pauline – those two were now like a double act. They were like the bailiffs – they only came in two's!

TJ looked over at Terry and said with surprise, 'What's feckin' Hank Marvin doing here?'

'Meet our new drummer.'

'What! You're having a laugh, Nick! This tour is mammoth. You can't change drummers without telling me. He's a keyboard player, not Phil Collins.'

'Look, Tone is having a rest. He's not been so good lately.'

'Do I look simple, Nick? He's back on the aspirin again, ain't he?'

Pauline added, 'I agree with TJ. You can't do this. He's nothing but a drug addict. You made a wrong call when you took him back into the band.'

'What's it got to do with you, Pauline? Didn't I read in the *New Musical Express* that your boyfriend got arrested in Paris for possession of coke? So don't tell me what we can or can't do. You've got too big for your boots, so back off and get back to Yarmouth with all the other carrot-crunchers.'

'That's enough!' said TJ. 'Let's not get personal, Nick.'

'Well, she thinks she's above everybody else. Do you know, you two could give Morecambe and Wise a run for their money.'

Terry butted in and said to Morecambe and Wise, 'Come with me – I'll give you a little demonstration.'

We followed Terry to the stage where the drum kit was already set up. He adjusted the kit to how he wanted it and said, 'If this doesn't suit you, TJ, I'll be on my bike.'

He then started drumming *Wipe Out* by the Surfaris. The whole theatre stopped what they were doing and listened to Terry. Unbeknown to us, the other band had turned up and were listening in the wings. What a performance – he was brilliant! He stopped after a few minutes and everyone clapped and cheered. The Canadian band stepped forward and the English bass guitarist, Pat, said, 'I didn't know Hank Marvin played drums!'

Their singer, Gerry, looked at his drummer and said, 'Randy, your drumming is crap compared with this English dude. I think we'll be taking him back home.'

TJ didn't say any more about drummers. He was well happy with Terry, and so were we.

I had a quick word with the Canadian band. 'Thanks for including us on the tour with you.'

They looked at me like they didn't know what I was talking

about. Randy the drummer said, 'Dude, we'd never heard of you until the promoter said you were our support act.'

'What about hearing us on a New York radio station and that's why you wanted us to tour with you?'

'We're not from New York, so we wouldn't have heard your record. And no disrespect to your band – we're not bothered about who the support act is as the fans are only coming to see us. In fact, if you're no good that's better for us.'

Randy and the rest of the band just walked away and I could hear them laughing. I thought, you arrogant bastards – you've just taken a pot at us. I told the others what had happened, and they weren't happy. Somewhere along the line we'd get our own back on them, that was for sure. We found TJ and tore into him about the lies he'd told us about the New York bollocks.

He was well embarrassed that he'd been sussed. 'Look, lads, I was just trying to build you up and give you the confidence you will certainly need for the biggest gigs of your life. I can see it has back-fired, so sorry about that, but remember I picked you as I know you won't let me down.'

To be honest, there was no answer to that, and in his own way he thought he was doing us a favour, so fair play to him. We moved on. We had to perform our sets in about half an hour but before that I needed to have a quick word with Pauline. I found her and said, 'I was out of order and apologise for what I just said to you. I'm really sorry and I do love Great Yarmouth and its carrot-crunchers.'

She looked at me for a moment and I thought she was going to blank me. Then she did the unexpected and gave me a cuddle. 'Somehow we've got to be friends again. I'm still very fond of you and ... well, we'd better leave it at that. And by the way, I've ditched the plane and what went with it and I'm using my Vespa again. I'm on the tour so perhaps we can start becoming friends again and leave the nastiness behind us.'

I gave her a cuddle and felt tears running down her cheeks.

Then TJ shouts out, 'Nick, quit the love-in – you're on stage in a few minutes.'

Still smarting from the rebuff of the so-called stars we all agreed that we might only be a support act but we were going to put on a show that would put pressure on this band to perform at the highest level to beat us. They looked the part with long hair and way-out clothes, but could they play? Terry had found out a few days before that they had only been put together nine months ago and were lucky that their two hits had been written by a top song-writer. They'd also had gigantic backing funded by the singer's Dad, who owned the record company. They hadn't played many gigs and playing live could put them under the microscope, so you never know – they might be found out. As a band we were tight as a drum – we loved a challenge, so they'd better watch out.

We went out on stage, plugged in and made sure we were ready to go. Every detail had to be right – this was going to be the highlight of our musical careers so far. I wished my Mum and Dad could see me now – they would be well chuffed. All the support staff and the Canadians stopped what they were doing to hear us play. We started off with a cover, just to get us going – *Hold Your Head Up* by Argent – and we really gave it the gun. Ray was superb on vocals and played to the small gallery like it was the real thing. A couple of girls from the catering team were in front of the stage and Ray came up close to them. They loved it, and the next few numbers were as good as it got for us. There was no messing about, fiddling with guitars and mics – we just played one number after another.

When we finished playing we could see people were impressed. There was plenty of clapping, cheering and a few whistles. We'd made our mark – now it was their turn. The kit they had was the best money could buy. They looked nervous as they got ready to play. They weren't good – in fact, they were polish. TJ looked a worried man when he came over to us.

'They've had two round-the-world hits but they didn't sound like this.'

Rick said, 'Do you remember Love Affair's *Everlasting Love* back in the '60s? Except for the singer, it was said that the record was played by session musicians. Perhaps that's the case with this lot.'

'Mind you, I saw the Love Affair live and they were an excellent band,' said Steve. 'They played that hit and you wouldn't have known the difference from the record, but I'm afraid you can with this lot, so you might have bought a pup, my son.'

We didn't hang about, as there was no need for us to stay – we knew we'd impressed. The next time we were going to see everybody was in a couple of days' time in London. The venue was ten times as big as we'd played before. What was great about this tour was that transport, hotels, food, etc, were all taken care of.

We had to get Terry a suit the same as ours, so we went down to Brent & Collins in Romford to have a butchers. They had some new Ben Sherman shirts that had just come in, so we treated ourselves. After that we had a nice frothy coffee in the Del Rio coffee bar. I then heard a loud shout from one of the terrible twins. 'Nick, I've missed you!'

Standing there was Mandy, now with a deep suntan, an even shorter mini-skirt than usual and a tight top that made her Charlies stick out even more. I have to say she looked horny.

'I rang you a week or two back from Spain and somebody said it's a wrong number.' She noticed Terry was with us and said, 'How's my little Hank?'

I looked at Terry, who went bright red, and I thought to myself, no, not you as well!

Mandy continued, 'Viv and I are going back to Spain tomorrow – just come back for my gran's funeral. And as it's our last night it would be nice to go out with a bang, so who's up for a party?'

The entire band were licking their lips and it was a 'Yes' from all of them.

The others were unlucky, as Steve me and the girls had a very enjoyable night round my house. It set us up for the tour.

♫ **16** ♫

The tour begins

We were hoping that we'd be on the main tour bus, which was like a house on wheels, but the main band had other ideas. They were the stars and it was only for them. They weren't sharing with anybody, which was fair enough, if that's how they wanted it. Even though TJ was the promoter, they ran the show and what they said went. I could only see trouble ahead. He'd hired us a small tour bus, a 12-seater, which to be fair was half decent compared with the crud we'd travelled in before. Des was driving us to the London show. With nerves jangling everybody lit up a fag– we'd ponced a couple of packets off one of the Canadian roadies. They were called Camel and after a while smelled like one, so it was back to the tried and tested Woodbine. The venue was massive. Even with 6 hours to go fans were already queuing. There was a billboard on the front with the Canadian band's name plastered all over it, but if you looked closely enough Modern Edge was in the bottom right, which is better than nothing. Des dropped us off by the stage door. There were loads of girls with their autograph books waiting for the headline group.

As we entered the stage door holding our guitars a couple of attractive girls looked at us and said, 'Who are you then?'

Ray said proudly, 'Modern Edge. We're one of the acts.'

'Oh, you're the support band that nobody's heard of. We're waiting for the real stars of the show.'

Rick couldn't help himself as he turned on the girls and said, 'If you think we're nobodies, you just listen to us. You'll know who the stars are after that. In fact, after the show Ray and I will be waiting for you outside the stage door, and you can show us your appreciation.' They didn't show, so you can't win them all.

We picked up with Jimbo, who was running around like a blue-arsed fly as the main act hadn't turned up yet. He was as good as gold with us and showed us to our dressing room. We wanted to get on stage as quickly as possible to run through the sets, which we did straight away. We just stood on the massive stage taking it all in, looking out to the rows of seating in the giant auditorium, which in a few hours would be packed.

Steve said, 'There's more tiers here than a feckin' wedding cake. It's mega. I'm shitting myself already.'

The sound man, Kev, made himself known to us. He was a bloke in his thirties and looked like a professor, but as soon as he spoke I knew he hadn't gone to Hylands secondary modern school in Romford where I'd gone – he was definitely a grammar school boy. He got down to business straight away and within half an hour we were going through the two sets. We played them over and over again until we were happy. As we were leaving the stage the stars turned up and Jimbo was having a go at them as they were well late for a sound check. We hung about waiting to hear them. They were in deep discussion with Kev, who didn't seem at all happy with them. When they started playing, what a racket! The noise was deafening! You could see what their angle was. They weren't a tight band and they were going to make as much noise as possible to combat their lack of playing skills – well, that was my thought, anyway. What surprised me was that beside their two big hits and their B sides they played a lot of covers that we played in our sets on the road. It wasn't our problem, so all we had to do was to concentrate on our own performance.

About 2 hours before the show we had food provided for us in the room next to the dressing rooms. The other lot were there first but they weren't very friendly, so we just blanked them. They might be stars but that meant nothing to us. Everyone seemed on edge, so Terry went into our dressing room and came out with one of my guitars and a small practice amp of mine. He plugged it in, then hammered out *Apache* by the Shadows. Because he looks like Hank Marvin, and smiles like him, it was wicked. Then he started doing the three-step walk, then went into *Wonderful Land*, with about 20 of us doing the walk across the room. Talk about an ice-breaker – everybody was now well relaxed, so much so that even the Canadians were starting to be friendly and were even talking to us, but it didn't last. Even though it was the biggest gig of our life, we always had the worry that if we looked at Terry and he gave us that grin we'd all fall about laughing.

The theatre was now packed, and the excitement, noise and anticipation from the teenagers could be heard everywhere. They were waiting for their heroes to appear on stage; unfortunately, there wouldn't be many who'd heard of us, so they would want us off stage as quickly as possible. The band always liked a challenge and we were ready for it. The buzzer went and we jumped up in the air. We were on. We shook hands with each other and Des said, 'Go out there and show them what a great band you are. This is your time – make it count.'

We all looked smart in our grey tonic suits and grandad shirts. We were ready, and as usual we ran on to the stage. A quick check to make sure that everything was plugged in, then, as I looked out, I was overcome with the vastness of it all. The crowd gave us a warm welcome and the first chord was struck. Ray is a showman and he was working his magic on the crowd. We were all bouncing about the stage and the crowd was with us. They seemed to like our music and us – we were having the time of our life. Our 15-minute set flashed by – we could've played all night. Ray thanked the crowd and as we walked off stage they gave us a great send-off. There were even a few screams. Back in the dressing room we said nothing for a moment; we were caught up in the emotion of it all. TJ and Jimbo ran in and were highly delighted with our performance. We had a quick drink, then went up to the first floor where there was a small balcony overlooking the stage, especially for the artists.

As they came on stage the crowd erupted. You know when it happens to you – you've made it. They went through their set and cocked up two or three of the songs; they weren't prepared well enough, but that didn't seem to affect the audience. The decibels were mega-high and, as we thought, covered a multitude of sins. They weren't that good; in fact, Dinky and the Dynamos sounded better than them. But with their publicity machine across the world funded by the singer's father, they couldn't go wrong. Were

we jealous? Feckin' right we were! By the end of the year they'd
be multi-millionaires and we'd still be pounding the beat up and
down the country for a few quid.

When they came off stage from their first set we were having
coffee in our dressing room before we went back on. TJ, Jimbo
and the Canadian's manager, Del, came in, and he said, 'Hi, guys!
What do you think of my band? You could learn a lot from them.'

That was enough for Steve, who stuck one below the belt.
'They're crap – without the dollars you've spent promoting them
they'd only be good for busking.'

I've never seen three people struggling for something to say
after Steve's outburst. TJ and the manager were lost for words and
walked out. Jimbo said to Steve, 'Why don't you just tell it how
it is, son?' Then he started laughing and we all joined him. As he
left he said, 'As it happens, you're right. I've been in this business a
long time and what you said about this band is spot on. But now's
the time to back off, otherwise you'll get all bitter and twisted.
Move on and show them what a great band you are. I know you're
looking for a record contract and I bet, by the end of the tour,
someone will come along and offer you a deal. You're on again in
a minute – remember what I've just said. Forget about everybody
else and just concentrate on yourselves.'

As Jimbo walked out the buzzer went, and I said to the lads, 'I
think that's great advice. Let's show them what we're made of.'

We had a little huddle put our fists together, then we were
ready to roll. The second set went well and we got a great
reception from the crowd, so much so that they wanted an encore.
They got one more number, which we shouldn't have done as we'd
been told to stick to the script, but hey, who cares? As we came off
Jimbo gave us a wink to say all right by me. TJ was still annoyed
with us for showing him up in front of the Canadians manager.

Taking Jimbo's advice we backed off the so-called superstars
and went for a few beers. It had gone well and we were looking
forward to the Glasgow show, even though Scotland in the past
hadn't given us the warmest of welcomes.

One of the London evening papers reviewed the show. They
felt the star turn was so-so and said our band was the bright spot of

the night. We were an up-and-coming band to look out for. After a good few years on the road, was it eventually our turn to be the main-line act? Only time would tell, but it would help if we got a record deal that might give us that No 1 hit.

As we made our way to Scotland we'd now gained a girl. Terry was a dark horse when it came to girls. He had this bird sitting next to him who looked like a librarian. Where he got her from I don't know, as there wasn't a library open late last night!

The Glasgow gig was held in an arena, and well over 7,000 tickets had been sold. TJ was as happy as a pig in shit, and good luck to him. Everything was going well in his world, but I could see one or two cracks appearing. We were getting ready for the show when I went into the toilet for a leak. Donny, the lead guitarist, came out of one of the cubicles holding a needle. He looked zonked, said nothing and just walked away. I mentioned it to the lads and suggested we should tell TJ. But their opinion was, it's not our problem, leave well alone. The show was huge for us and we had a great night.

The tour moved on to Newcastle, then Manchester, and it was packed houses all the way. At Manchester I got Ann, Julie and their mates from Hull some tickets, but only Julie came with her friends as Ann wasn't well enough, which was a shame. She was one of those girls that, if she'd lived nearer, I would have loved to see her on a more permanent basis We were coming up in a few weeks' time, so I'd be able to see her then.

We did try to get a bit closer to the Canadians, but they just didn't want to know. We liked a drink, but they abused it; a couple of times some of them were half cut when they went out to play, and it showed in their performance. The lead guitarist and singer were now so drugged up, it was an embarrassment.

A worried TJ took me to one side when we reached Cardiff. 'Nick, we've got three gigs to go and this star band are really taking the piss. You know some of them are on drugs, plus there are more bottles of Jack Daniels going in that dressing room than the whole of feckin' Canada. Reviews haven't been that good. If they fail to appear at these next gigs I'll be bankrupt and my business will be finished.'

Unfortunately, TJ's fears came back to haunt him. The night before the Cardiff show the Canadians' lead guitarist, Donny, was found unconscious, needles and drugs were scattered around his room, and he was rushed to hospital. The next morning he was still in a bad way, but the doctors thought he'd pull through. TJ, Jimbo and the group's manager were in a right panic about that night's show. A heartless TJ insisted that it must go on – all he saw was pounds, shillings and pence.

Our band were on stage practising when Pauline came in. TJ wanted to see me. I went into the Canadians' dressing room, which was as quiet as a grave. The band and their manager were shell-shocked, and all the cockiness had gone as TJ spoke.

'Right, come in, Nick. Now, we know what's happened to Donny and thank God he's going to pull through. We've all had a chat. The first option was to pull the plug on the rest of the tour. The second option, after chatting to Del and Jimbo, is that you fill in for Donny.'

'What! Let's get this right – you want me to play lead with these guys?'

'Yeah, for the three shows that are left.'

'That's a tall order.'

The English bloke from the band, Pat, stepped forward and spoke. 'Nick, I know you don't rate us and that's a matter of opinion. Listening to you play we would have no hesitation in working with you. If we pull out we're going to let thousands of people down and even though you think we don't care, we do.'

I thought about it for a moment. I knew a lot of their material relied on the lead guitar, as they only had a bass and some keyboards, which Gerry played. Most of their stuff was not too difficult to play and their two big hits didn't have a lot of chord changes. It was an opportunity to put my skills to the test, and I was up for it.

'OK, I'm in. But we've got to rehearse all day to get it right. We've got to be focused, no drugs, no alcohol, not even going for a wee.'

They laughed at the last comment and seemed relieved, especially TJ, who had the most to lose. And that's what we did right up until an hour before the concert began. Steve and the rest of the lads were well jealous, wishing it was them playing. They were well supportive, though, and wished me well. Not many people knew, except for the inner sanctum, about Donny. It was imperative that it didn't get out. The spin was that he had appendicitis.

It was a huge venue with a capacity of well over 4,000 people. I was bricking it – it's all very well to talk the talk, but could I walk the walk? If any good had come out of this it was that their attitude had changed towards us, and us to them. With minutes to go the buzz was electric as Modern Edge was ready to play Cardiff. The last time we'd played here we got booed off and run out of town, so we were hoping for better things. The buzzer went and we ran on to the stage, except Steve, who fell arse over tit. He will wear these long winkle-pickers – it wasn't the first time he'd done it and it wouldn't be the last. The crowd erupted with laughter and Ray said with a grin, 'He's falling over himself to play Cardiff!'

The set went well and I went from our dressing room to the Canadians. They looked on edge, as I was, because I could cock it up for them tonight. I changed from my suit to the T-shirt that they wore. My hair was as long as Donny's and my height near enough the same as his. TJ, Jimbo and Del, their manager, wished me luck and Pauline gave me a cuddle and a kiss. I could hear the crowd getting restless waiting for their idols – I wished I was one of them. I now know how that bird from Hull that we met at the Sidmouth holiday camp felt when we called her first reserve, because that was me tonight.

We strode purposefully onto the stage to a backdrop of one of their hits. The lights pinged on from every angle. The roar and screaming from the crowd was deafening. My inclusion in the band so far had caused no ripples. If this was what being famous was, I'd have as much as it could give me. For a second my bottle went as the other band members looked at me to say, don't forget you start this one. I had my favourite 1965 Fender Stratocaster apple-red guitar and it was my time to put my name on the map, even if it was only for three gigs.

What a night it was as I played with this star band! I loved every minute of it and, if I say so myself, I didn't let anybody down. Everyone was well pleased with the show, especially TJ. Both bands and all of the back-up team went out on the turps afterwards and we partied till the early morning. It was a pity that it took a drug overdose to get everybody singing from the same hymn-sheet. Donny wouldn't be able to play the last two gigs, so yours truly was in the hot seat again. The review the next day actually hit one of the national papers. The write-up was mustard, and I even got a mention about replacing Donny. I felt on top of the world.

I was looking forward to playing Bristol, not just because of the show but also for the chance to meet up with Shelly and the girls from the hair salon. I gave her a bell and made arrangements to meet up a couple of hours before the gig. We met in the bar of our hotel, which was just around the corner from the theatre in the middle of Bristol. Even though we were all knackered, by 11 o'clock in the morning we were rehearsing furiously. There was still a lot of work to do, even though there were only two gigs left.

I met up with Shelly, and she looked gorgeous. There was good news and bad news. All the other girls from the salon were coming, but the bad news was that Anita and Jenny were also coming, having booked at the last minute. When I told Shelly that I was playing with the main band she couldn't believe it. She told me that she was leaving the salon next week; she'd got a job as a hairdresser on a cruise ship. I was pleased for her, and she promised to keep in touch. After the show, TJ had booked a nightclub for everyone in the tour team plus a few guests. Shelly and the girls were definitely invited, but not Anita and Jenny. I told her where the club was – something else to look forward to besides playing.

Bristol went well, with bands on top form. After the show, with TJ funding a night out, we headed for the club. Shelly and her mates turned up and within minutes they were dancing with Ray, Rick and Steve. Terry still had his librarian girlfriend, and they were both looking a bit haggard – too many late nights reading books! The Canadians had pulled the top-of-the-range birds, who looked like they'd just come out of modelling school. TJ looked very dapper in his new Lord John clobber, and he had a face from the past with him. Tammy hadn't made any progress and was struggling for work, so was creeping back to see if he could get her some gigs. Knowing him, there'd be a price to pay! Ray had clocked Tammy when she came in and I could see him trying his luck again. Des was happy as he'd tugged the merchandise girl. It was turning into a great night, then I noticed Anita and Jenny, who had somehow crept into the club. I went over to Steve and pointed them out to him. I'm not normally nervous around girls, but these two were different. Street-wise and owning their own business had made them a bit savvy. Shelly had gone to the loo and Anita quickly came over to me.

'Look, Nick, I really want to have a chat with you about the incident that happened in Reading.'

'I really don't think there's much more to say about it. Your bloke and that moron Rupert were cowards the way them and their mates set upon us. By the way, where are the intimidators tonight?'

'They're not really like that. They've gone to a boxing tournament in Bristol and are going to pick us up later.'

Shelly came back and wasn't happy about Anita being there with me, and made it known. 'We're not at work now, Anita. Nick and me are enjoying each other's company, so three's a crowd.'

'Look, Shelly, it's not like that. I just wanted to apologise to Nick about the bust-up with Simon and Rupert, that's all.'

'Well you've done that now, Anita, so I'd appreciate it if you'd leave us alone.'

'OK. Sorry to have butted in.'

Anita can be fiery but on this occasion she looked quite crestfallen as she walked away from us. I must admit my feelings for her had never gone away and part of me still wanted to be with her right now. Steve came over. Jenny had said the same thing to him, but Steve, being Steve, saw an opportunity and they started dancing together. Anita went back to the other girls from the salon. It was getting near the end of the night and people were getting ready to go when Simon and Rupert appeared at the doorway. Rupert was not a happy bunny when he saw Jenny smooching with Steve. He went over to her and roughly pulled her away, saying, 'What are you dancing with that nerd for?'

'It's only a dance, nothing else, Rupert,' said Jenny.

When Jenny said 'Rupert', all the band members fell about laughing. He stood there boiling over, and Simon and Anita joined him. Then Steve, who'd now had far too many pints, laughed at him and said, 'Rupert, it's a bastard trying to get to Scotland in the depths of winter, especially on a wild goose chase!'

I followed up with, 'I bet the bed and breakfast people were well chuffed being woken up at 3 o'clock in the morning!'

The penny didn't drop for a moment, then the faces of Rupert and Simon said it all.

'It was you two bastards who set us up!' said Rupert.

'You'll wish you'd never done that,' piped up Simon.

'Oh, grow up Simon,' I said. 'You're pathetic – just admit it you both got done up like kippers.'

'How could you have done that, Nick?' Anita said.

'Get real, Anita – do you think that after they attacked us that we were going to take it sitting down? We're more subtle than that. We don't use violence, just brains, which these two dickheads of yours clearly haven't got.'

All the boys in the band surrounded them and continued taking the rise out of them. What surprised me was that Jenny didn't stick up for Rupert, but Steve rubbed his nose in it when he said, 'I think it's about time you left, as this is a private party and gatecrashers are not welcome. I bet Scotland is off your holiday list now.'

Steve turned his back on them and walked away, then suddenly Rupert, who'd clearly lost the plot, tried to land one on him. As he made his move, Ray appeared out of nowhere and stuck a right hook on his nose. He went down like a sack of Murphy's spuds. Ray turned on Simon, who looked shell-shocked, and said, 'I'd suggest you take this idiot home and don't ever threaten my friends again or you'll have me to contend with.'

Anita started crying. 'It should never have got to this.'

I put my hand on her shoulder and said, 'I agree, but you can't just take it from bullies.'

Simon said to me, 'Don't touch my girlfriend!'

'Do you know, Simon, you don't know what a lovely girl Anita is. I'd walk away now before Ray does an Ali shuffle on you.'

Simon picked up Rupert and said to Jenny, 'Come on, let's go.'

But she replied curtly, 'I'm not coming. Rupert and I are finished. I've had enough of him taking me for granted.'

With that they both left, with Rupert holding his nose, which was still oozing blood, followed by Anita. Anita gave me a quick glance and I could see tears running down her face, which made me feel very sad. After that Steve and Jenny were back on speaking terms – and a little bit more! It was a pity about the violence, but that wasn't our doing. Ray's boxing always came in handy. I remembered my boxing skills. I represented my house team in a boxing tournament at school, and after winning my bout my PE teacher, Mr Powell, said I could represent the school. When I found out that my first bout was against the Essex schoolboy champion, a knock-out specialist, my bottle went. Nobody lasted in the ring with him for more than a few seconds. I gave it a miss and my replacement, a mate of mine called Peter, got knocked out in 15 seconds.

Soon it was the last gig of the tour back in London. When you'd played to vast crowds, the thought of only playing to 100-plus in a couple of weeks' time was like drinking champagne followed by cream soda. The venue was magnificent, and it was a great finish to a memorable tour. Straight after the gig the Canadians caught a flight back home; they were touring the East Coast of America as soon as they got back. Donny, their lead guitarist, recovered from his overdose, so that was good news. TJ was as happy as could be – he'd pulled off his first large tour with a main-line band. To be fair to him, he was well happy with our performance and gave me plenty of praise for stepping in at the last moment. It was sad to say goodbye to all the back-room team. There is a saying 'memories are made of this'. Thank goodness we had this to look back on, as the next journey for the band was going to be difficult, to say the least.

♫ 17 ♫

After the Lord Mayor's Show

We weren't playing again for just over a week, which was handy as we needed to find a new drummer. Terry had been a diamond helping us out, but he had his own band and they were booked for some gigs in East Anglia. We met at Monty's cafe to talk about getting a drummer and any other issues that needed to be sorted out. As we sat down, Monty, looking more like a thug than normal, shouted out, 'You didn't buy one of Ronnie's watches, did you, lads?'

'Why's that, Monty?' said Des, who was laughing his head off.

'Ronnie's watches were the headline act on Shaw Taylor's *Police 5* last night. In fact, the Old Bill were here this morning sniffing around.'

We all looked at our new watches, took them off and shoved them in our pockets. While we were eating our Belgium buns and drinking tea, a dark shadow in the shape of Sammy appeared over Rick. He looked up to see who it was, gulped, and the cherry from his cake caught in the back of his throat. You'd have thought he'd got whooping cough from the noise he was making. While thumping Rick's back, Sammy said, 'You need to get that cough sorted out, son. I need a little chat with you. We can either do it in front of your mates or we can go in the back room.'

Now, the back room in Monty's had many uses, as a place to plan a job or, if someone had been a naughty boy, a place for a slap. With panic showing in his face Rick immediately said, 'We can talk here Sammy, I'm among friends. What do you want to talk to me about?'

'My sweet little daughter, Carol, who I idolise.'

Rick went into another coughing fit. 'She's a very nice girl, a credit to you, Sammy.'

'You're a toe-rag, son, and don't give me all that bullshit. A little dickey bird has whispered in my ear that you've been seen out with her.'

'No, not me, Sammy – she's too good for me.'

'Do you know, son, I don't whether to give you a spank now or wait till that new motorway up the road is built. You'd look good in a concrete overcoat. I'm going to have a little think about it. In the meantime, remember I've got more spies out there than MI5.'

Sammy gave Rick one more hard stare, thumped his back and went back to sit with his mates.

Rick had a worried look on his face, and said quietly, 'Carol has missed her monthly. We're thinking if she's up the duff, how are we going to tell her Dad?'

Des said, laughing, 'On the phone from a call box in Australia!'

'Look, let's forget the sideshow,' I said. 'We need a drummer pronto.'

Then Ray said, 'I've got some good news and bad news all mixed up in one.'

'Well, what is it then?' asked Steve.

'Well, it's a bit complicated. Billy has broken up with Gloria – she's been playing away with the singer in his band. The band is finished because Billy broke the singer's jaw, and it's hard to sing when you're all wired up. Billy's back living with his Nan in Romford and he's available straight away.'

'I've only just got my hearing back. Looks like I'm going to have to get that hearing aid after all,' said Steve.

We all voted for him to come back into the band. He was a good drummer and knew all our material, so it was a no-brainer. As we were having our second cup of tea, Ronnie stuck his head around the door. He looked as shifty as a fox as he made sure the coast was clear to come in. He was wearing an Andy Capp, black sunglasses and his favourite crombie. He always wore it when he was carrying swag around – he'd had a few extra pockets stitched into the inside. He came over to us, looked right, then left, and said, 'Hello, lads – is Monty about?'

With a straight face Des said, 'A time bomb has just gone off. Monty's upstairs with the Romford Flying Squad. They've caught him with one of your watches and are searching the gaff. By the way, Shaw Taylor sends his best.'

'What're you on about, Des?'

'Didn't you see *Police 5* last night?'

'Nah, I was at Romford dogs last night. I own a cherry hog called Slick Mover. It came in first at 10 to 1. Made a right killing – the bookies were well sick.'

'I'd suggest you get on that greyhound's back, because those dodgy watches were on *Police 5*.'

'You're jesting, Des!'

'I ain't, and Monty didn't look too happy, my son.'

With that Ronnie was out of trap one and was not seen on the manor for a week or two.

'I liked the time bomb, Des,' said Ray.

'Yeah, quite apt I thought.'

We met up with Billy and had a day's practice to bring him up to speed. The good news was he didn't seem to be hitting those skins so hard, which helped everybody's hearing.

It didn't appear that the tour had helped us get much more work. TJ was happy with what we'd done, but now, because of the success he'd had, it appeared he had bigger fish to fry. He was now booking the big boys on the circuits. As he kept saying, we were a '60s band and we'd always get work, but it would be limited as more progressive bands were out there. If you were a 16-year-old in 1964, you loved the '60s music, but now those teenagers were 24-year-olds and had different music tastes. We'd had this conversation before; we liked the music we played, but realistically how long could we carry on with our heads in the sand? Fortunately, none of us were married or had long-term girlfriends, so money wasn't the driving force. Mind you, we could all have done with a bit more, and sooner rather than later it would be crunch time, but the travelling jukebox goes on and we still had lots of gigs to fulfil.

The first gig after the tour tested our willpower to go on. After the Lord Mayor's Show, etc ... and if you've ever been to Grays, Essex, you'll know what I mean. We were playing at a social club in the roughest part of the town. The seating was an assortment of chairs that you sat on at school and the tables looked like they were from a canteen. At the back of the wooden hall was a long bar, which normally told you that they were there for a good drink and you were the background music. The stage, if you could call it that, was a number of pallets nailed together. The curtain that went across the pallets looked like a black-out curtain from the war. The hall backed onto the Thames and the draught that whizzed through the cracks of the wooden structure would give a bleedin' penguin pneumonia.

The steward, who looked like old man Steptoe, brought over a tray of light ales for us. As he cuffed his nose, which put a bogie as big as a walnut on his already stained sports jacket, he said, 'We don't want it too loud, otherwise people can't talk. And another thing – a couple of the old boys like to get on the mic and do a bit of Frank Sinatra at the end of the night.'

'You're joking, mate! We don't do talent spots. If people want to talk, why have you booked us? Our last gig we played to thousands,' said an irate Ray.

It went straight over his head. 'Cor, you won't get that many in here tonight. Top whack hundred and fifty, if that.' He then shrugged his shoulders and sauntered off, smoking his Golden Virginia roll-up like he didn't have a care in the world.

Billy laughed and said, 'Since I left I can see you've gone up in the world...'

'On your bike, Billy,' said a very annoyed Steve.

We didn't even bother with a sound check and only brought in a couple of amps. It was nearly 7.30, and I peeped through the curtains to see how many punters were in. I couldn't believe what I saw, and turned around to the boys. 'Come and have a butchers at this.'

'There's nobody sitting down. It looks like a bleedin' chair exhibition!' said Rick.

We all looked out and most of the punters were milling around the bar. There were a few ladies sitting down and some pesky kids of about 11 who sat right in front of us drinking lemonade and eating crisps. When we looked through the curtain they gave us the 'V' and wanker sign.

How we got through the night I don't know. It was one of the worst gigs we'd done. Next day I phoned TJ and asked him if it was an April fool's joke.

Our next gig was a freeman's. As mentioned before, we had to let him know if we were playing any gigs he hadn't booked, but he didn't have a problem with us playing this one. I got the impression that, as long as we did his shows, we could do whatever we wanted, which in a way meant he couldn't give a monkey's about us. There was some good news, though. Carol wasn't pregnant, so we'd saved some money on a wreath for Rick.

On the girl front, I tried to get hold of Ann in Hull, but was told that she was in hospital. Hopefully there wasn't too much wrong with her. Pauline was now going out with another musician, so she was out of bounds at the moment. Shelly was on the high seas giving the old girls a cut and a rinse. Mandy was still in Spain, so the girl front was a bit bare. Steve was seeing Jenny when he could. Fortunately, the break-up with her boyfriend, Rupert, had no bearing on her friendship and partnership with Anita. Steve did say when he last met Jenny that Anita sent her best to me.

The freeman's gig was back at my old senior school that Steve, Des and I attended. The headmaster got in touch to ask whether the band would mind playing to raise some money. He'd got another band playing as well. One of the junior kids had a condition that needed urgent medical care, and it appeared that only in America could this illness be treated, and it didn't come cheap, so they needed some funds to get him there. We were only too pleased to play and help the young lad. After that we had some well-paid gigs that included some corporate shows for a few top companies.

A couple of days before the school show Steve and I went down to Southend to have a bit of fun. As you do, you meet a couple of girls, and Kate and Eve were good fun and we spent the day with them. They lived on Canvey Island so, being gentlemen, we took them home in Steve's rust-bucket Consul – definitely a Friday afternoon motor, as they say. We had a little snog, then dropped them off. Next day was a Sunday and the good news was that Steve's bird had an empty house for a couple of hours in the afternoon. It didn't take too long for Steve to pop upstairs with

Kate. My girl, Eve, wasn't like that, so I was like a spare part at a wedding. Fortunately, Steve and Kate came downstairs before her Mum and Dad appeared. Her Dad, who seemed a friendly bloke, came in with a bag of shellfish.

'Do you want to stay for a cockle tea, lads?'

Steve, who doesn't think before he opens his mouth, said jokingly, 'It's been cock all afternoon.'

Her Dad only took a few seconds to realise what Steve had said before he kicked us both out of the house.

The school charity show was being held on the school field, where a small stage had been erected. As soon as I entered the school that afternoon memories took over. I had not been a model pupil. I recall that Steve, Des and I had somehow broken a swing over the local park, and the park keeper took our names. Next day, in front of the assembly, our names were called out by the headmaster, a man well over six foot and built like a tank – Welsh, as they all were then, and a former rugby player. In front of the other 400 pupils he said that we'd brought shame to the good name of the school and would be punished. We then had to walk out of assembly and stand outside his office. As we left, everybody was taking the piss, including that wanker Dinky. As we stood there, we were shitting ourselves as we knew what was coming. We had put an exercise book down our trousers to try and stop the pain. I was the first one to be called and he gave me a bollocking about the school bit again. On his wall he had a glass cabinet which housed his canes. He decided which one he was going to use, gave it a quick flick, and said, 'Boy, don't take me for a fool. Get that book out of your trousers now.'

As I took it out he said, 'For that you will get an extra stroke. Bend down.'

I bent down and closed my eyes, swearing to myself that I wouldn't cry or scream. I can feel the pain now as he launched the assault. The dust from my trousers was like London smog. My knees buckled as every stroke hit its mark. I had six of them and the pain was horrendous. As I stood up the evil bastard said to me, 'Let that be a lesson to you. I don't ever want to see you again, Sheldon.'

I passed Steve and Des without saying a word and went straight into the toilet and safety. I dropped my trousers and looked in the mirror at my burning arse. The cane marks were like a London underground map, with all the different colours. I never went back in there again and fortunately within a few months he'd moved on to another school to inflict more pain to some other poor sod.

Another thing I recall being punished for was not my doing. We had a lady teacher who was a right old spinster. She meant well but she was from another era and couldn't control the '60s kids, who were now much more rebellious and ill-disciplined than a decade earlier. She'd read us this book called *The Prisoner of Zenda*, which was about as much use to a 14-year-old as a chocolate fireguard. Every day she would read this book for 15 minutes. At break time two little urchins were going to put a stop to this. They lifted some floor boards in her classroom and chucked the book down the dark hole. Being the horrors they were, they set a light to it, then chucked some water over it from a fire bucket. When the teacher found out her prize book was missing there was an inquest and a little teacher's nark said, for whatever reason, that it was Steve and I that had taken it. That was that – we were now in the frame. Punishment was given by a younger teacher – the old girl was too old to dish it out herself. She got this wooden ruler out, put it on its side and whacked it across our knuckles, two on each hand. To say it hurt was an understatement! I never did find out who put us in the frame for that. Also, when we were chatting in class and the teacher wanted your attention he would throw a wooden blackboard duster at you. If that hit your head you knew all about it.

Anyway, back to the gig. As we unloaded our gear at the back of the stage I couldn't believe who was standing there – Dinky and his Dynamos.

Steve said, 'What're you lot doing here?'

'We're the main event, so move over and let us set up.'

With a daytime gig like this you wanted to go on first, as it always tailed off later, and if there was a bar you ended up playing to yourself, so you'd got to be first on. Dinky, his right-hand man Bruce and the other three were taking no notice, so the heavy guns came into play. Up stepped Ray and Billy, the dynamic duo. They just folded their arms and stared at Dinky and his lot. The stand-off lasted a matter of seconds, then Dinky decided that it might be a good idea to let us go on first. As he took his gear off the stage I whispered to him, 'Coming back here reminds me that some little snitch stitched me and Steve up. *The Prisoner of Zenda.* Does that ring any bells…?'

Dinky went red, then white, stuttered and said, 'Not me, Nick – I was never a grass.' He was off that stage as quick as lightning.

We set up and fortunately it was a nice day. The crowds were coming in and spending money. Lots of our old mates were coming, including a few girls. It was always a shame that our school was boys-only, but across the playing field was an up-market girls' school – in other words, they had brains. So if we needed any tuition on our P's and Q's we'd meet after school.

The gorgeous Diane came over to me while we were setting up. 'Hi, Nick – your band is getting more famous by the day. Fancy you going on tour with that Canadian band – that's really cool.'

'Great to see you! You're still looking delightful – perhaps…'

'Sorry, I'm spoken for, but you never know what the future holds.'

'How's your brother Pete? Still over the pond?'

'He is, but he's coming back from the States in about three months' time for good. He's got a new job lined up with a record company.'

'That sounds ace. With his background as a music magazine journalist, it'll be right up his street. Perhaps he can help us.'

'Not going so well on that front, then?'

'Not really. A bit of interest from one or two record companies but nothing concrete yet.'

'I'll have a word with Pete when he comes back and arrange a meeting nearer the time. Isn't it about time you played some music?'

We got the show on the road and, with a few hundred people both watching and dancing, it was a great afternoon. Before Dinky's band came on there was an auction and a raffle to raise some more money. I'd been in touch with the English bloke, Pat, from the Canadian band about any mementos he could send. He and his band were diamonds – the next day they sent a guitar signed by all the band members and some signed photos by air freight. What was funny was that Ronnie, who had also gone to this school, turned up with his mate, Spider, so-called because he had a bald head with a tattoo of a spider on it. Spider was also an old boy, but not for long as he had a spell in an approved school. They'd brought along half a dozen watches to put in the raffle.

Des said to them, 'You can't put these watches in a raffle, Ronnie.'

'Don't worry! I've put them in Timex boxes. Anyway, it's for a good cause.'

'What have you brought for the raffle, then, Spider?'

'A couple of bottles of Bell's whisky, Des.'

'Hang about! Wasn't there a break-in at an off-licence in Collier Row last week?'

'Nah, not me. I got the whisky over in Spain on the old duty free lark.'

Ronnie scratched his head and looked at Spider. 'Leave it out! You haven't even got a passport.'

The guitar fetched mega-money at the auction and we were pleased to help. The funniest moment was when the raffle prizes were given out. There were a couple of policemen in their bright new uniforms, old boys of the school. One of them was putting on his new watch he'd just won.

We stayed a little while to listen to Dinky and the Dynamos play to an almost empty field. It didn't help that when they started the heavens opened up.

♫ 18 ♫

Thank goodness for the fourth emergency service

The next couple of weeks were both terrible and tragic. In fact, that's an understatement. We played a gig in London's docklands, a pub venue that you normally wouldn't play for any money. TJ said we'd be doing him a favour as the publican was a mate of his. Another fib. Later we found out it was Tammy's father's gaff. Things you have to do for a leg-over.

It was one of these pubs where they put sawdust on the floor to mop up the blood. It was so dark in there you needed a torch to see where you were going. The geezer was a typical East End publican, plenty of chat, plenty of gold and someone you wouldn't like to upset.

'The stage is over here, lads,' he said.

Stage? It was another pallet job.

Ray then said, 'Is this what it's come to, playing in a khazi to a lot of piss-heads? I remember when I was someone a while back, singing to thousands of people at some of the biggest venues you can get.'

'Oh, leave it out, will you, Ray?' said Billy. 'I'm miserable as it is – I don't need you bellyaching. Any more of it and I'm going to jump in the Thames.'

We all had a laugh and set up. We were using our small amps as we didn't want to blast the locals. The only good thing here was that the publican wasn't stingy with the beer. For a small place it was packed out and the night wasn't that bad. As we were packing up we committed a cardinal sin in the music business. We'd just loaded up and the landlord called us back to give us some drink money. Unfortunately, we all went and left the van unattended. It was only a minute or so, but when we walked out the van and all our gear had gone. We just stood there feeling physically sick. Des was beside himself – he felt he was responsible for the loss. What was a sickener was that all our guitars were in there. Normally, Steve and I don't let them out of our sight. I could've cried. Des was like a man possessed as he ran up and down the road looking for the van. It was no good – it was long gone.

We went to the local police station and reported the loss. The sergeant at the desk said, 'Sorry, lads, if it ain't nailed down it gets nicked round here. I'm afraid the van and its contents are long gone. Hope you're insured.'

Next day we reported the loss to the insurance company. Straight away they were trying to find ways of not paying out. My prize Fender guitar, Steve's SG Gibson bass and Rick's brand-new Korg keyboard had all gone. That didn't include amps, mics, and Billy's Ludwig drum set. Steve and I met Des down at Monty's. He was devastated and inconsolable. Then Steve had a moment of inspiration. 'What about "Red Adair", the fourth emergency service?'

It took a minute or so for the penny to drop. Then Des shouted, 'Of course – Jack! He said if we need any help to get in touch with him after we helped him out with his daughter's singing at his home-coming party.'

'Is he still out of jail?' I said.

'As far as I know. Let me have a word with Monty.'

Des called Monty over and told him our problem. He was more than helpful. In fact, he said he'd put the word out to find out who'd done it. He wasn't so sure about contacting Jack, though, as he was well up the food chain and something minor like this he probably wouldn't bother with. After a bit of persuasion Monty relented and went off to make a phone call. About 15 minutes later he called Des over and took him in the back room, where he gave him the phone.

'Hello, Jack, it's Des, Frank Smith's son. I'm really sorry to trouble you. We've got a problem and I wonder if you can help. If you remember, at your party you said if ever you could do us a favour, just ask.'

Jack laughed and said, 'I do recall that. One of the band called me Red Adair, the fourth emergency service. So what fire do you want me to put out for you, Des?'

'The band played a gig at a pub in the dock area in East London last night. We left the van with all our gear in it for a minute and some toe-rag has tea-leafed it.'

'Where exactly was this?'

'Outside the Ship & Anchor down The Highway.

'Make and model, and by the way, Des, I wouldn't ever leave anything with wheels on down there.'

'I've heard that before. It's a dark red Mark 1 Ford Transit 1300. It's got trade plates and the reg number is ACD 865. It's got a dent on the wing and another on the back door with a scrape on the driver's door.'

'Des, do you take it stock car racing? Leave it with me and I'll see what I can do for you. Be lucky.'

Des came back and gave us the SP. There was no more that could be done now. With Monty and Jack on the case, and hopefully the police, we'd just have to wait. Our next gig was in two days time, so something might come up by then. I had to tell TJ, who was sympathetic but it was our problem, and gigs still had to be done. I then spoke to Terry, who had lots of spare gear. It helped that his Dad owned a music shop. He would lend us whatever we wanted, and as the next two gigs were pretty low key in small halls, we wouldn't want too much.

That night I got a late-night phone call from Pat in Canada. He had some sad news. Donny had finally done it and overdosed. He thought he'd let me know before it hit the national press worldwide the following day – they were that big. It didn't feel right when I said to him that the signed guitar had made a lot of money for the young lad to go over to America for treatment. I wished him well, then went and found a bottle of brandy and gave it a right tonking.

The next morning I woke up with a blinding headache courtesy of a bottle of 103 Spanish brandy. Steve and I went and saw Terry to sort out some equipment. It was like Aladdin's cave as we went through his goodies. He had a large room in his parents' house where he kept it all. Terry was saying that his band weren't sure that they were going to continue for much longer. Like us, they had no record deal and they were fed up of travelling all over the country for shiny buttons. He'd been offered a lot of session work, which was a good earner, but the band had been together for a

number of years and he didn't want to let them down as he was
their main man.

The thought of never seeing my guitar again and the rest of the
gear was gut-wrenching. The band decided to meet at Monty's in
the hope that Jack would come back to us today. Terry had a spare
few hours so he came along with me. As we walked in, Monty was
in fine fettle – he must've had it off somewhere. As soon as he
saw Terry he shouted out to the other punters, including his son
Sammy, 'Hang about! Hank and the Shadows have just walked in!'

He picked up a broom and started gurgling away with *F.B.I.*
and playing air-guitar with the broom. He then went into the
three-step walk, got it wrong and fell arse over tit on the floor.
We didn't laugh, just a slight grin – didn't want to upset him.
Then Carol came out from the back. Sammy's eyes narrowed as
he clocked the response from Rick, who looked the other way.
Everybody was down and Des was as depressed as I'd ever seen
him.

As we were slurping our tea we talked about the death of
Donny, which was tragic. Carol kept looking at Rick, but he was
trying to ignore her. Sammy smelled a rat and was about to come
over to Rick when the phone rang. We jumped up in the air, and
Monty picked it up. Was it Jack? No, it bleedin' wasn't, just one
of Monty's cronies. The call lasted for ages. We were all looking at
our watches – it would have helped if the timepieces had worked.
That wanker Ronnie… Monty put the phone down and shouted
to us, 'This place ain't the bleedin' WI. Start ordering or start
walking.'

After two breakfasts and oodles of tea we got up to go. Then
the phone rang again. Monty, who'd got a limp after his exploits
with *F.B.I.*, walked painfully over to get it. He picked it up,
listened, and beckoned Des over. Minutes later Des came back
with a grin on his face and said,
'Good news and bad news.'

'Come on, Des – good news first,' said an excited Ray.

'Well, it appears all the equipment subject to us checking it has
been found in a lock-up in Canning Town.'

Everybody cheered and hugged each other, and Billy shouted,
'Thank goodness for Red Adair!'

'What's the bad news, then?' said Steve.

'The van is a wreck and is only fit for the scrappy.'

'Well, that's OK,' I said. 'We can claim for that on the insurance. It was nicked and we've got an incident number from the police.'

Des went quiet and coughed nervously. 'Well, there's a slight problem on that score.'

'What do you mean by that?' said Rick.

'Well, I meant to get around to it…'

'Don't tell me it wasn't insured, Des, please.'

'Don't worry, Nick, I've got another van already from Spider – got it for a song. I'm paying for it.'

'You're having a laugh, Des!' said Ray. 'Spider only nicks 'em – he doesn't buy 'em.'

'Who were the culprits, Des?'

'Two rogues out of Stepney. Jack put out some feelers and offered a drink to anyone who had any info. It didn't take long to find out who it was, as he runs the East End. Jack pulled them in, they put their hands up and he said they had a week to come up with the dough to pay for the van. He gave them a slap and he's expecting the money Friday.'

'What a result! We owe him,' I said.

'Well, there is a sting in the tail…'

'There always is, Des. What is it?'

'It's his daughter's birthday soon and you've been selected to provide the entertainment and he wants her to sing a few numbers.'

We all laughed, but it had to be done and that would certainly be a night to remember.

All the equipment was there when we picked it up from Canning Town. One of Jack's right-hand men was there to help. As we left this bloke said, 'Don't forget to pencil Jack's daughter's birthday into the diary. We'll let you know the venue.' He added, 'She's looking forward to singing with you again.' As he walked off we could hear him laughing to himself.

Des got the Commer off Spider, and it looked too good to be true. I hoped it wasn't hooky – I didn't want to think about it. We got the money from Jack and that helped pay for it. I bet the two blokes who nicked our gear would be thinking twice about thieving on Jack's patch again without him knowing.

A few days later I was having a lay-in after a late-night gig in Margate when the phone rang. It was Neil, Ann's brother from Hull.

'Hi, Nick, I've got some bad news. Ann isn't well at all and it looks like it's just a matter of time.'

I couldn't get my words out, I was so shocked. 'I knew she was poorly but I didn't think it was that serious.'

'Look, Nick, I know it's a big ask with all your band commitments, but Ann is desperate to see you. I just wondered…'

'I'll be up there straight away, Neil.'

We had no work for a couple of days – even if we had I'd have gone anyway. I rang Steve and told him the news and that I'd be off the radar for a couple of days. He was as upset as me. He said he wanted to come up as well, which was well decent of him. He said he'd drive and he'd be round in under an hour. As we scooted up to Hull in his newish Ford Zodiac we were lost for words. At our age you don't expect this to happen to young friends. It was ironic that I had been working on a song called *Life Is Not Forever*, which I had high hopes for.

We got to Neil's late afternoon. The family and Ann's best mate, Julie, were beside themselves with grief after visiting her.

Neil explained. 'Initially Ann went in hospital for a blood disorder, but after more tests it was found that she had leukaemia. Unfortunately, it's very aggressive and she now only has a matter of days to live. She is conscious and that's why she asked me if you would come and see her.' He said we could go to the hospital now.

I asked him, 'Does she know she hasn't got long to live?'

'No one has said anything, but I'm sure she knows it's just a matter of time.'

As Neil and I made our way to the hospital I was feeling really apprehensive. The thought of her struggling to live – it didn't bear thinking about. We stopped off and I bought her some red roses. We arrived at the hospital and made our way to the ward where she had a room of her own. Neil stayed outside while I went in to see her. As I walked in she was half asleep. She looked up and saw it was me.

'Nick,' she said weakly as I gave her the flowers. 'You've made it, and they are lovely roses. It's so good to see you. Julie and the girls told me what a great show it was in Manchester. I wish I could've been there.'

'Ann, forget about me – it's you I've come to see.'

She moved forward and put her hand on mine. 'You were the first proper boyfriend I ever had. That week in Sidmouth when we first met was very special, especially now when I haven't got much time left to live.'

'Don't talk like that, Ann.'

'It's true, and you so understood about my alopecia.' She gave me a weak smile. 'Do you remember when you crept into my bedroom at home and my Mum said about the woodpecker attacking the apple tree?'

She then coughed and motioned for me to give her the glass of water by the side of her bed. She took a sip and continued. 'I hope you have a good life, Nick. Live life to the full – you don't know what's around the next corner.'

I gently took her in my arms and we cuddled each other as tears streamed down our faces. I whispered in her ear, 'Another time, another world, another life, we'll meet again, Ann.'

'I hope so, Nick.' She smiled. 'I'll be waiting for you.'

She fell asleep in my arms and I gently rested her head back on the pillow. She looked so peaceful as I left her.

A nurse came in. 'I'm so glad you came to see her. She said to me that you were the only boy she really cared about. She'll rest in peace now.'

Two days later Ann died peacefully surrounded by her family. On the day of the funeral we had a gig at Colchester and I said to the other lads that I was going to the funeral and would they mind if I cancelled the show? None of them minded, but as luck would have it Terry had just got back from a few gigs in the Midlands and said they'd do it for us, which was well handy as I didn't like letting people down. I rang TJ and said Terry would do it for us, so could he tell the venue about the change of group? He then said just the worst thing he could've done at that moment. 'We can't just change the group like that overnight, Nick. It's a client we're letting down.'

'For once in your life, feck the client, and stop thinking about your wallet. This funeral is more important to me than a shed full of clients.'

I slammed the phone down. Within a few minutes he came back on the phone and apologised, but then said, 'We can't pay Terry and the Tanks the same money – they're not as well known as you.'

It's times like that when you know who your friends are. The entire band wanted to go to the funeral to pay their respects. Most of them had known her, even if it was just for a short while. I thought that showed real class and I was proud to be part of the band. Des hired a six-seater and we went up early in the morning. The church service was very moving, and there wasn't a dry eye in the place. From there she was laid to rest at a quaint old church on the outskirts of Hull where her grandparents were buried. As the congregation stood around the grave I threw a single rose onto the coffin and muttered, 'Another time, another world, another life…' We went to the wake for a short while and met up with her family and a lot of the footballers that Steve and I had played with.

As we were about to leave, Neil took me to one side and said quietly, 'My sister really loved you. I know it was a short relationship but it meant the world to her.'

'And me, Neil. I wish I'd got to know her better, but the distance and my lifestyle with the band made it difficult. I'll never forget her and what a brave girl she was.'

'Please keep in touch, Nick, and I'll be looking out for that No 1 hit in the charts.'

As we made our way home I reflected on what I'd said to Neil about my lifestyle and the band. I'd heard that from one or two girls I'd got close to, Anita being one of them. Was it an excuse, or was I so wrapped up in the band that any relationship would always come second? As I fell asleep in the car my thoughts were with Ann, a very brave lady.

♫ **19** ♫

It's Father Christmas time

Gigs around Christmas were always a good earner. We had half a
dozen booked, mostly in London. As mentioned earlier, they were
for company Christmas parties. The first one was a livery hall in
the city of London. There are well over a hundred of these halls
in London, and they come under the banner of trade associations
and guilds, like the Worshipful Companies of Merchant Taylors,
Brewers, etc – there is even one for musicians that goes way back
to 1350. It would be an experience to play at one of these halls.
We would be playing for a firm of stockbrokers located in the
Square Mile – EC1, 2, 3 and 4.

TJ was acting like a school teacher when he said, 'It's suits
and ties, no uncouth language and the volume must be at a level
that they can still hear themselves talk. There will probably be
free drinks, so no taking advantage and getting legless. Ladies are
strictly forbidden. If you recall, the last time you played at one of
these shows, Rick shagged the managing director's wife.'

I butted in, laughing. 'Get the facts right – it was his daughter!
Is there anything else that we serfs have to do?'

'Yeah, don't be late. And lastly, Tammy will be making an
appearance, so she'll want to sing a couple of numbers.'

'You're taking the piss!'

'Behave, otherwise she'll be on your next tour.'

We both had a laugh at the threat of Tammy singing with us.
TJ thought he was the only one that was making whoopee with
her; little did he know that Ray had charmed himself back into
her arms and was working the nightshift round her flat.

On the night of the show we left early. It was a Friday and
we didn't want to get stuck in the city traffic. Luckily, we got
into the hall early and set up. It was a magnificent building. The
architecture was stunning – even for us heathens it was something

to be admired. We had a quick sound check and asked one of the organisers to give the OK on the sound level while we played. He seemed happy, so now it was a waiting game. We had on our suits and slim ties and our winkle-pickers were shining! While we were waiting some of the catering staff, mainly girls, came in. After a few minutes they came out of the back room wearing their black and white outfits, looking really horny. The idea at these occasions was to get one or two of the girls on your side so they'd supply the drinks behind the stage and top us up as needed. Our good-looking scouts Ray and Rick were on the case, immediately mingling with the girls. It worked, and we had a couple of girls, who were best friends, to sort out the drinks for us.

There were about 200 coming that night. Our eyes were out on stalks as they drifted in – some of the ladies looked amazing in their new outfits. We felt like the minstrels of olden days as we got ready to play. Dawn, a well-spoken lady in her thirties, was our point of contact. She had a posh voice, a slim figure and wore plenty of gold. She was the PA to the senior partner at the stockbrokers. Everything was in place as we started to play – it was going to be a good night.

After about an hour, with one more number to play before the first break, everything changed. A number of policemen came in and said we had to leave everything and evacuate the building immediately. No one seemed to take it too seriously, until they said it was a bomb threat. Then people started rushing out of the exit doors, including us, at a fast rate of knots. As we stood outside in the freezing cold the news came through that the party was over because it would take too long to check every nook and cranny before giving the all-clear. Fortunately, it was a false alarm, but with all the bombs going off in England at the time it was better to be safe than sorry. We picked up our gear the next morning and, to be fair, the company paid us the full whack and a bit on top.

After we'd played all the other Christmas shows I relaxed at home for the few days before Christmas Day. We had a break till New Year's Eve, then we had a good earner coming up. I was sitting in my favourite chair in my jimjams having a cup of tea when there was a knock at the door. No peace for the wicked,

I thought, and got up to answer it. Standing there was May, my next-door neighbour, with a large sack by her side and a worried look on her face. May and her husband Harold, both in their sixties, were the salt of the earth; they had lived there since the year dot. They'd been great friends with my Mum and Dad, and when I was away May came and checked everything was OK with the house and was always bringing round homemade cakes. I asked her in.

'You look worried, May. Is there a problem with Harold?'

'Yes, there is.'

'Do you want me to call a doctor?'

'He's ill, but not seriously. He's got a bad case of the trots – not unexpected as he gave the Double Diamond and pickled eggs a right pasting last night down at the Legion in Hornchurch. He'll never learn.'

'So what can I do for you, then, May?'

She looked at me and I knew that whatever it was would not be to my advantage. 'Well, young Nick, you know Harold dresses up as Father Christmas for the local schools. They have a Santa's grotto and he dishes out the presents.'

'Yeah, they love him around here – but what's that got to do with me?'

She took a deep breath, looked at me and said, 'In just under an hour Santa's sleigh is going to arrive and take him to the local school in the High Street where Father Christmas is going to be handing presents out to the little dears.'

'Little dears? I wouldn't like to be Harold going there – the kids are monsters.'

'How can I say this, Nick? Look, Harold can't go, somebody has got to go in his place. He doesn't want to let anybody down.'

'May, please tell me you don't want me to be Father Christmas.'

'Nick, you'd make a great Santa! You get on well with people and you'll be really helping Harold out. It's only for two hours.'

'I hate kids, and that lot down there are bloody murder. That's why they built the borstal up the road, to accommodate them a few years later.'

May gave me a pleading look. 'When you come back, Nick,

there'll be a nice Bakewell tart waiting for you.'

As I was putting my Father Christmas outfit on I was saying to myself, 'Why am I doing this?' May was fussing around me. She'd brought a blanket to wrap around me to bulk me up. I looked in the mirror – thank God the band couldn't see me now! In the distance I heard loud Christmas carols playing. I went to the door, and a flat-bed lorry stopped outside. On the back of it was a model reindeer and a sleigh for Father Christmas to sit on. The whole street was out to see what the commotion was about, including Steve. As the neighbours saw me come out of my house the piss-taking started.

Steve couldn't believe his eyes. 'Got a new job Nick? You do know you look a right wanker? I'm going to have to phone the boys up!'

'Don't you dare! I've got all these bloody presents to deliver.'

I jumped on the sleigh and we headed off to the school. I must admit I got a right buzz waving to everybody in the High Street and getting plenty of waves back. It wasn't so good when one of reindeers' little helpers braked hard and I nearly fell arse over tit. As we entered the school my bottle went when I saw the young kids waving at me, and some others sticking their tongues out.

The headmistress greeted me, and when she heard my voice she looked worried. 'Where's Harold?'

'He's had to go to Lapland to get some more presents.'

The old bat wasn't impressed and gave me the evil eye. I said, 'Look, it's me or nothing – unless you've got another mug in mind.'

She took me to Santa's grotto, a shabby little room with decorations that looked well past their sell-by date. I eyed up the two elves who were Santa's little helpers, then sat in the chair. I said to the elves, 'So what happens next?'

'When the little cherubs come in, you ask them what they want for Christmas, listen for a few seconds, then Brenda and I will give them their presents and send them on their way.'

'Have you done this before? By the way, what are your names?'

'Yeah, lots of times. We're from the local college. We're training to be teachers, and this gives us an insight into what we're letting ourselves in for. Oh, by the way, it's Daisy. What's your name and what do you do?'

'Father Christmas, and I deliver presents.'

'Ha, ha, ha.'

'It's Nick and I play in a band.'

'What's the band's name?'

'Modern Edge.'

Daisy was impressed. 'Really? You're playing at our college at the beginning of the New Year.'

Then all the niceties stopped when the first little monster entered the grotto. He had ginger hair, was aged about seven and already looked like an apprentice thug.

'Hello, what's your name?'

'Why'd you want to know?'

'It would be nice to know your name so I can give you a present,' I said.

In a strong London accent he pulled a face and said, 'There's no such thing as Father Christmas. It's all a bleedin' con. Just give me a present and I'll be off.'

I was warned about little bleeders like him before I went into the grotto, and advised that I must hold my temper when they kicked off. Unfortunately, I have a quick temper and I don't like having the Michael taken out of me.

'You don't believe in Father Christmas? Then piss off.'

He looked at me in disbelief, as did the elves. I picked up one of the bigger presents and wiggled it in front of his beady eyes. 'Now tell your mates if I have any more verbal from any of them they'll get the same treatment. I'll say it once more – you do believe in Father Christmas, don't you?'

'Of course I do! I was only joking.'

'That's a good little boy. Here's your present – have a very nice Christmas and don't forget when Santa comes down the chimney on Christmas Day you must leave me a mince-pie and a glass of sherry.'

As he walked out he turned around and said, 'You must be joking, mate. That fire will be full on and as you come down you'll get a burnt arse.' He poked his tongue out at me and ran out of the room.

Daisy laughed. 'Father Christmas, I don't think you'll get the job next year.'

All three of us had a good laugh. I toned it down a bit after that, and got through the morning till there was only one more child to see. Brenda went outside to fetch her in. As the door opened a little girl aged about six sitting in a wheelchair came in with her mother. I moved over to her.

'Hello, what's your name?'

'It's Sally.'

'Now, what do you want Father Christmas to bring you on Christmas Day, Sally?'

She put her little hand on mine and said so sweetly, 'Father Christmas, can you bring me a magic wand that will make me walk?'

I looked at her mother who, like me, had tears in her eyes.

'If I can ever find a magic wand that will do that for you, Sally, you'll be the first one to have one. What I have got, though, is some lovely presents for you.'

There were quite a few presents left over, so I made sure she was well looked after. As the elves gave them to her she said, 'Thank you, Father Christmas – you won't forget that magic wand, will you, because one day I want to walk and then I can help my mummy because when she gets older she might want me to push her around.' She gave me a cuddle, then added, 'I won't forget the mince-pies, Father Christmas, for you and your reindeer.'

As I made my way home I felt very humble that a little girl was looking for a magic wand to make her walk. I hoped they would find a cure for whatever she had and her dream would come true.

Christmas can be a bit lonely if you haven't any family around you, and I was going to be on my own, but was happy about that as I could relax and not worry about travelling up and down the country. The other lads were spending Christmas with their families. They all asked me round for Christmas dinner. I thought I was going to be on my own until I got a phone call from Pauline. Like me, she had no family left, and the relationship with her boyfriend had gone pear-shaped.

'They only want you for one thing, Nick,' she said.

That's a hard one to answer, as blokes are near enough all the same. She asked me what I was doing over Christmas. When I told her I was on my own and that she was welcome to spend it with me round my place, she was up for it. The next day, as soon as she arrived, we went shopping for Christmas dinner. It was straight down to Romford Market looking for a bird – a feathered one. We came across a stall selling fresh turkeys, but there was nothing on the table – must be in a freezer. Pauline thought it was a really good price for one. After agreeing the price he took us to the back of the stall where his van was parked, and undid the door – loads of turkeys! Unfortunately, they were still alive and kicking!

We spent a terrific Christmas together and agreed we'd see more of each other. The New Year was nearly upon us and we were hoping that dream of a No 1 hit would be a reality in the coming year.

♫ **20** ♫

A record deal at last

On New Year's Eve our mates from our schooldays always met at lunchtime at our favourite coffee bar, La Nero. It was a ritual that we'd kept going since the early '60s. All the band members came, including Des. His Dad, Frank, had a court case hanging over him regarding some dodgy motors; unfortunately he was renowned for cutting up two motors of the same model and welding them together to make one.

Alec, king of the Mods, was there with his Lambretta TV 175, and Wendy and Roger, who I remember winding up. Back in the '60s Rog decided he wanted to smoke a pipe. On his birthday we got him a new pipe and some baccy. He stuffed the baccy in, lit up, and was away with the fairies. Unbeknown to him he thought he was puffing away on Dunhill Mixture, but it was wacky baccy. Ronnie was his normal self. He was now knocking out Ben Sherman shirts, but looking closely at the label it read 'Len Sharman', another con. Ted, the guv'nor, was still there, as was the AMI Continental jukebox. It was all '60s and new '70s songs, including a couple of ours. To the sound of *Layla* by Derek and the Dominos we enjoyed the banter of our mates and caught up with the latest news over our frothy coffees. One of my favourite ladies, Diane, came through the door together with a friend, Anne. Diane saw me and came over; we sat down at one of the blue plastic Formica tables, I got her an espresso and she said straight away, 'I'm glad I've seen you. I've got some good news for you.'

'You've packed your boyfriend in.'

'Well, I have, but it's not that. Remember I told you about Pete coming back to take up that job with a record company? Well, he's coming back sooner than we thought. In fact, he's back in two weeks' time. I did have a word with him about your band trying to get another record deal. What he's said is that once he gets his feet under the table with the new company he'll contact you and at least give you an audition, but it must be your own material, no covers.'

'That's great news, Diane. You're a star! You seem to know a bit about the music business.'

'Didn't I tell you I'm a shorthand typist at the same company he's joining?'

Before we left we had a moment's silence in memory of our great friends, brother and sister Rod, Carol and Jimmy, who tragically died in a car accident in 1964. We were all very close, and it made you appreciate life.

We were back on the treadmill when we played a New Year's Eve bash at a political party's club in Gidea Park, a more upmarket part of Romford, once known as Romford's garden suburb. It was only a stone's throw from where I lived, so I walked there, which meant I could have a few sherbets. The boys were buoyant about the pending audition, so there was a feel-good factor in the camp. The only downside was the lack of girls of our age, mostly 30-plus, and too old in our books. I have to say it was the most boring New Year's Eve party we'd played. I hoped that this wasn't the start of things to come in the New Year.

We drifted through the next two or three months but still hadn't heard from Pete about the audition. We did try to bell him and left messages, but he didn't call us back, so that looked a non-starter. It was now March and we were looking forward to the next two gigs, which were going to be full houses.

For whatever reason, Exeter liked us. In 1965 we did a great gig there, and so far every year we had returned for a two-nighter in a nice theatre holding 600 people. A couple of days before we set off there was bad news. Des's Dad got six months for the cut-and-shut job and a couple of other offences. The outcome of this was that Des was going to have to look after the business while his Dad was away on holiday. He was gutted at letting us down; Ronnie offered to roadie for us, but we gave that a miss. It was no big deal driving down there and setting up; in fact, it meant more money in our bin. The weather forecast for the week wasn't good – a promise of storms was all we needed.

We made sure the van was taxed, insured and roadworthy
and not a cut-and-shut, then off we went, with Billy driving the
van. The usual song we always sang when we headed down to the
South West was good old Cliff and the Shadows' *Summer Holiday*.
Steve was well happy – he was meeting Jenny from Reading at the
gig. Rupert was a long-lost memory, so happy days for Steve. We'd
got ourselves a nice hotel. We'd booked well in advance and got a
cracking deal on the price – a bit of cream for a change, instead of
some wafty B&B. The storms hadn't arrived yet and we had a good
journey down. It was like meeting old friends when we entered
the theatre. Vince, the sound engineer, was there to greet us; we'd
known him since our first gig here. Then Doris, one of the ladies
on the catering side, shouted out, 'I've got your favourite, Nick!
Plate full of Wagon Wheels.'

We gave the Wagon Wheels a hammering with our tea, then
we set up for the night's show with the help of Vince. He still
had his own band, the Vincent Five Blues Band, who were all out
of Sidmouth. Sidmouth brought back memories of Ann at the
holiday camp, and another tear was shed. Vince was as sound as a
pound as he helped us set up, and I have to say that the sound he
produced was as good as any on the planet. In fact, he was always
in demand with the top groups. We had a sound check and were
busy on the stage with a couple hours to go before showtime when
Steve got a call to say that Jenny was downstairs. He was off like a
bolt of lightning.

I was looking forward to playing that night, especially as all the
tickets had been sold. Steve came up and said he was going to the
La Ronde coffee bar, and asked if I wanted to join them. I really
didn't want to, but he insisted. As we walked in, Jenny was already
getting the coffees in, then I saw the reason why he wanted me
there. Anita, looking very nervous, was sitting down at one of the
tables.

I said to Steve, 'Look, mate, I really don't want to complicate
my life again, especially my love life, what's left of it. Just give her
my regards – I'm going back to the theatre.'

'Nick, she really just wants to bury the hatchet and clear the air and be friends again.'

'Bury the hatchet? Her boyfriend would have killed us a while back, or have you forgotten about that? No, sorry, Steve, she's a top girl but I don't want to get involved again.'

I went back on stage and played some songs on my acoustic. There was nobody there, just me, my guitar, and 600 empty seats. It was a way of relaxing and shutting everything out. I played some new numbers that I had written, including *Life Is Not Forever*. The lyrics took in poignant parts of my life, especially the loss of people close to me. I was lucky – I could express myself in my music, especially with this song. After about 10 minutes I was about to put my guitar away when I heard somebody clapping in the auditorium. I looked up and there was Pete.

He came down and said, 'You want to ditch the band, Nick, and go solo.'

'What are you doing here?'

'First things first – I apologise for not getting back to you. The easy answer is that my boss, Mr Asciak, is staying at a hotel in Plymouth for a few days.'

'Where's that name from?'

'He's Maltese. Anyway, I wanted him to hear you play live in front of an audience to see whether he thinks you're worth taking a chance with for a record deal. I wasn't going to tell you that we were coming, so keep schtum to the rest of the band members. I'd better get going now before I get spotted. I won't see you after the show, but I'll be in touch later. Have a good one tonight.' He then laughed and said, 'By the way, I hear you make a great Father Christmas!'

'How do you know about that?'

'That'd be telling.'

He left and I walked back to the dressing room with a bit of a dilemma on my hands. Do I tell the boys that a record company is looking at us, or do I keep quiet and treat it as a normal gig? As I walked into the dressing room everyone was bubbly, so I thought I'd leave well alone.

Steve came out of the bog and said, 'You're bit of a knob.'

'What do you mean by that?'

'You could have said hello to Anita.'

'I don't need you to tell me what I should or shouldn't do. With your track record with birds I'd keep well quiet.'

'Come on, lads, no throwing handbags at each other,' said Ray.

At that precise moment I could have walked out on the band. The stress of keeping them together for years was telling on me. My personal life with my Mum and Dad dying in my teens, losing my close friends Rod, Carol and Jimmy in that minibus accident, the loss of Ann, the little girl in the wheelchair, Tone, now a serious drug addict, and Anita, who I still had feelings for. I felt right at that moment in time that there had to be more important things in my life than a '60s band now past their sell-by date. I lit up a fag, went downstairs, stood outside the theatre and inhaled deeply.

I was deep in thought when Rick joined me. 'Are you all right, Nick? You're not your usual self.'

'No, I ain't, Rick. I think the time has come for me to bail out of the band and get my life together. Time is passing me by and I need to recharge my batteries and maybe move in another direction.'

'We all go through this, Nick. My Dad going to prison, Mum's cancer and the continuing shuttling from one town to another trying to make the charts has its affect.' He then laughed and said, 'And trying to dodge Sammy, Carol's Dad, who wants me dead, hung and quartered.'

We both laughed and Rick put his arm around me. 'Come on, Nick – shake a leg! Let's get out there and put on a show to remember.'

Billy came out, looking worried. 'Is everything all right, guys? We're on in 10 minutes.'

'Yeah, I'm having an old fanny moment, that's all,' I said.

As Billy went I thanked Rick for our little chat. It was now time to do what we did best – play music.

As we walked onto the stage to a great reception I bent down to check my set list and noticed that Jenny and Anita were in the front row. Anita gave me a wave and I smiled back.

Everything came together as we pounded the beat on stage.

We didn't realise that the new numbers we had written were now right up-to-date in the groovy '70s. There was a freshness about our playing and, with the new material, the '60s, where we'd been before, was now being overtaken. The gig was one of our best, with a long encore – it didn't get any better than that.

The band went back to the hotel to celebrate. Fortunately it was not far away, as a storm had kicked in with driving rain. Steve said that Jenny was staying the night, but that Anita was going to stay at her parents' house in Dawlish, which with the bad storm could be a problem. He was having a drink or two with Jenny, while Anita sat next to them looking like a gooseberry.

I went over to her and said, 'Would you like a drink?'

'That would be nice, Nick.'

'Port and lemon.'

'You've got a good memory.'

I got the drinks in and we sat on our own in the corner of the bar. Straight away Anita said, 'Look, Nick, I've never been able to apologise properly about the nastiness with Simon and Rupert. I'm truly sorry about that.'

'Talking about that, where's lover-boy tonight?'

'Please Nick, can we move on? If you really want to know, Simon is on a rugby tour in France for a few days. I came here for the show, then I was going to my Mum and Dad's for a few days in Dawlish, but with the weather like it is, that could be a problem.'

'Why have we got this love and sometimes hate relationship?'

'Look, Nick, there was a time I could've spent the rest of my life with you but...'

'I know what you're going to say – with my lifestyle, etc, it would never work. What if I got a nine-to-five job and was home every night. Would that make a difference?'

'Try me, Nick.'

I was lost for words, then, changing the subject, she said, 'I thought the band, with all your new songs, was great. Any joy with a record contract yet?'

'No, but there is something on the horizon. We'll just have to wait and see where it takes us.'

We sat together like long-lost friends and chatted for a couple of hours. Steve and Jenny had gone to bed, and there was no way Anita could get to her parents' house that night. Should I try it on? She could be vulnerable. Was that the way to go? I didn't think so.

'Look,' I said. 'I can't let you go to your parents' tonight with the rain pelting down and thunder and lightning everywhere. You can have my room and I'll bunk in with one of the band.' She gave me an old-fashioned look. 'I mean it,' I continued. 'There's no hidden agenda, but I would like to see you tomorrow. Come to the show in the evening – is that a deal?'

'It's a deal, but no funny business. I know what you're like, Nick Sheldon.'

I took her up to my room, cleared up the mess and said that I'd see her for breakfast. I kissed her lightly on the cheek and left.

Now, which animal was I going to share a room with tonight? I knocked gently on Rick's room, and heard a shuffle. That's good, I thought, he's awake. He opened the door with just his boxer shorts on.

'What the feck do you want, Nick?'

A girl's voice in the background said, 'Who's that, Rickie?'

'Don't worry sweetheart, they're just going.'

'What's going on here?' I had a quick peek through the side of the door. Not a pretty sight – it looked a shocker. 'Where did you get that from? Is there a zoo around here?'

'Piss off, Nick.'

The door was slammed in my face. Next stop, Ray. Again, I gently knocked on the door. No reply. I knocked again. Same result. Must be on an away night. Billy was now my last hope. I knocked and he came to the door in a pair of colourful pyjamas.

'Sorry to trouble you, Billy – can I kip down somewhere in here?'

'No problem, Nick. Women trouble, then?'

'Yeah, something like that.'

As I walked in, the smell of putrid farts was making me heave. 'Billy, your guts must be rotten. What've you had to eat?'

'Double Chinese, but I was still hungry so I went to the late-night chippy and had a large cod and chips.'

I met Anita for breakfast. She was still surprised I hadn't tried it on, and so was I! We got on really well – it was like old times. The storm had passed and it was now bright sunshine. She was off to her parents' house for an hour or so, but said she'd come back for lunch. When she came back she drove us down to Exmouth in her Mini. We had a bite to eat at the Pavilion on the seafront and a walk along the beach. I really wanted to be with her, but I could understand her not wanting to be with someone unreliable. She wasn't a young teenager any more; she was a sophisticated lady. We did have a cuddle, but it started raining so we went back to the theatre.

While Jenny and Anita did some shopping it was time to go over a few of the new numbers. Before we started I told them about Pete and his boss coming yesterday to look us over. They were a bit annoyed that I hadn't told them, but they soon got over it. It was another great night and another packed house. After the show Steve and I had a drink with the girls. Steve couldn't wait, and he and Jenny disappeared for the rest of the night and morning. Anita and I were getting on really well, but it was late.

I said to her, 'It's getting late and it's half an hour's drive to your parents' place.'

'I don't have to go, Nick.'

The next morning I woke up and Anita had gone. She'd written a message on the mirror with lipstick: 'Nick, let me know when you have a nine-to-five job. Love Anita xxx.'

After Exeter things happened pretty fast. Pete got in touch to say that his boss was impressed, and we were invited to their studio to put down some tracks. After that, if it went well, they would talk about a contract. I rang TJ and told him the good news.

He said, 'What's in it for me?'

'I think it should be what's in it for us, like more money if we get a hit record.'

The phone went dead, but Pauline rang back and wished us well.

The next gig was Annabel's birthday party. Jack had been on the blower giving us the SP and making sure that we were focused for the event. It was to be held at a country club near Epping. We didn't want any cock-ups, so the day before we went up there and it all looked good – it was an impressive place to play. Then little niggles set in. On the way back the van started to play up. Ray had been starting a cold, and on the day of the gig he lost his voice. Rick could take over the singing and we roped in Terry from the Tanks to help us out. It got worse when the van wouldn't start. Terry went back home and we used his gig van.

When he started it up, Steve said, 'Christ, it sounds like a Sherman tank.'

We all laughed, except Steve, who hadn't twigged he'd just cracked a funny. 'What're you all laughing about?'

'You tonker! What's Terry's surname and the name of the band?'

The penny dropped and he said no more.

What was great about that night was that they were all young people of our age at the party. Jack greeted us warmly and we thanked him for getting our equipment back. There were a lot of guests coming. I remembered my 21st birthday – I'd spent it with the band at a greasy spoon on the A1.

Everything was in place, a good sound check and we were ready to play. Des turned up and helped us, apologising for letting us down over the last few weeks. We were wearing our new '70s bell-bottoms and paisley shirts. Now, you can imagine a band of randy blokes ogling the birds as they came in. What a feast – there were some right little darlings, including Carol. Hot pants galore, the new fringed mini-skirts and tops so tight it was indecent. The teenagers were all bringing presents piled up on four long tables; their parents would make sure the presents were tip-top, not wanting to disrespect Jack's daughter.

Billy shouted out to me, 'Oi, Nick, I bet this reminds you of your Father Christmas days.'

There were a few suspects there, including Monty, his son Sammy, and Ronnie not wearing a hat for the first time ever. He was going a bit bald on top and Steve shouted out to him, 'Ronnie, they do some nice syrups down Petticoat Lane!'

'Bollocks! How's that watch I got you?' He certainly knew how to hurt someone.

Jack ran over and said, 'Annabel's coming in – play "Happy Birthday" now.'

We did as we were told and played it as she walked in. What a state – she was a well-built girl, and the top was so tight her breasts looked like oversized melons. The hot pants were so tight-fitting you could see the outline of her knickers. If she got on top of you, you'd need a bleedin' respirator.

It was now party time and we ramped up the sound. The first set was a scream, followed by some nosh and plenty of free drinks to wash it down with. Before the second set Jack came over and we thought, oh no, he wants his daughter to sing – and he did.

'Can Annabel sing a number, boys? It is her birthday.'

It all went quiet, then Jack said, 'I know she's crap, but one day you might have a daughter and you'll know what I mean.'

We somehow got her through *Your Song* by Elton John. Luckily he wasn't there, otherwise he'd have wished it wasn't his song. The whole night went off really well until Sammy caught Rick with his hand down Carol's top at the back of the hall. It was like the Keystone Kops as he chased Rick across the fields clutching a wheel wrench.

Two days later we were in the studio in London with Pete and his recording people. This was our big opportunity to nail one of our new numbers. For two full days we went through our paces. Mr Asciak was there for part of the time, but basically left it all to Pete. Within a matter of days there was a recording contract on the table.

Out of all the numbers we played, the one they really liked was *Life Is Not Forever*, which was handy, as I had written it. Lots of things started to happen. Our contract with TJ was up for renewal. Even though he could be a pain in the arse he never messed us about with money, we always got paid on time, and we had no problem renewing our contract with him subject to us all agreeing, which we did. His dip into main-line bands and organising major tours hadn't worked out, so he was pulling back from that and the Rolls-Royce went. Instead, he'd concentrate more on bread-and-butter bands like us with no risk of losing vast amounts of money. With more than 100 bands on his books he wouldn't go short.

Tom, Steve's Dad, as usual came with us to cross the T's and dot the I's. With our record deal done, TJ would liaise with Pete about tours and other aspects of the band's progress.

We were now getting frustrated that our single still hadn't been released. The initial euphoria had gone and we felt we were getting the bum's rush. We kept phoning Pete but he was never there. Mr Asciak, his boss, was back in his home country on business. At least TJ was giving us plenty of work. We were now adapting to '70s music, but with bands like Mud, the Rubettes and Sweet setting the world alight, it was going to be hard work.

After a long journey back from a gig in Burnham-on-Sea, I was having a lay-in when I had two phone calls one after the other. The first was from Anita, who I hadn't spoken to since Exeter.

'Hi, Nick, it's Anita. How are you?'

'What a nice surprise! I was going to ring you, but I thought maybe it wouldn't be such a good idea with Simon in tow.'

We had a nice friendly chat – she was adorable. I knew deep down that this was the only girl for me – it was either her or the band. At that moment it was her, and I knew the two wouldn't go together.

Before I could say much more she said laughingly, 'Nick, let me know when it's that nine-to-five job time. You take care and look after yourself.'

Before I could say anything she'd gone. I was going to ring her back straight away and tell her that she was more important to me than the band and I wanted to be with her. It might have been one of the biggest mistakes of my life, but I didn't phone her.

When the phone rang again I was hoping it was Anita.

'Hi, Nick, it's Pete. It's the news you and the band have been waiting for. The record is being released next week, and the publicity machine is full on.'

The record hit the shops and was moving up the charts at a fast pace. The band was now going to be one of the big boys. Two weeks after its release we were having breakfast in Monty's prior to a good gig at Stratford Town Hall in East London when the phone rang and Monty shouted out, 'Nick, it's for you!'

As this was our second home, most people used the number to

contact us. I answered the phone and after a couple of minutes I was back, totally gobsmacked.

Steve said, 'Who was that on the blower, Nick?'

'You won't believe it, lads – we've got a No 1 hit! A tour is being arranged right now to take it around the country. We've never played Malta before, have we…?

♫ Epilogue ♫

The band played together until the mid-'70s. On a journey back from a gig in Holland it was agreed that we'd taken it as far as we could, and it was the right time to call it a day. There was no animosity and we're all still mates.

We never achieved a Top 10 hit in Britain, but we did go to Malta! Rick had outstayed his welcome in England and left to live in Spain. Sammy had finally had enough of him going out with his daughter Carol, and made it quite clear he was public enemy number one and it would be in his best interests to disappear. Ray and Billy reformed the band they had before they met us, Bad Brakes, with the other original members. They're doing well and have a record deal. Steve and I are still gigging part time with Terry of the Tanks fame. His band disbanded, so we go out with him and his ex-drummer Josh as a four-piece now and again. Steve landed some session work and I'm also playing in another band that plays a lot in Europe, which I'm enjoying.

Tone is now on the road to recovery. He's been living with his sister, Penny, our ex-drummer, and her son, Robin. It's still a mystery as to who the father is, and we look at him closely when we meet up with her to see if there is any resemblance to any of us. Des is full time in the motor trade and has a site in Seven Kings High Road. He comes on gigs with us and does the roadie bit, which he loves doing. He's still involved with the 'chaps', but that doesn't concern us any more, I hope.

Monty had a heart attack and had to take life a bit easier, so his son Sammy took over the running of the family businesses, legal and not so legal. Mind you, Monty's still barking orders out in his cafe. Ronnie has a stall in Romford market knocking out tool boxes and anything else he can get his hands on.

I still keep in touch with Neil, Ann's brother from Hull. He comes down and stays with me sometimes and I take him out to watch the local football. Ann is still in our minds, and it's nice to talk to him about her. Talking about football, both Steve and I have got ourselves fit and play for Rainham Town, a semi-professional side in the Athenian league, when we can.

The terrible twins, Mandy and Viv, are now off the radar. They've both settled down and are married. For how long I don't know – both their mothers have been married three times. Pauline left her job with TJ because she was offered the manager's job at the Regal Theatre, Great Yarmouth, where she'd worked before. We keep in contact, but she is now engaged, so it's purely a chat.

We left TJ's company when Modern Edge disbanded, but he's still going strong and we meet up now and again. Dinky is still playing with the Dynamos when he can find somebody to book him.

I lost my chance with Anita. She's now engaged to Simon, and I don't speak to her any more, which is a shame, but it's all my own fault. I did ring her up and told her I had a nine-to-five job, but it was too late.

Steve is still going out with her mate Jenny, and they're off to Australia in a month's time for a holiday. Shelly came back to Anita and Jenny's salon to work; the engagement didn't last, which was good for me as I see her quite a lot.

Big Al came back to England, but I've lost contact with him. I'm sure our paths will cross again.

Jack, aka 'Red Adair', went back to prison for a few years, so no more gigs for the criminal fraternity.

The band had a great time but, like everything else in life, nothing lasts forever. Eleven years of our lives were spent living the dream. Little did we know that nearly 40 years later Modern Edge would reform. But that's another story, told in my book *The Sixties Boys on Tour*. A promoter phoned me at home late one Friday night in 2013 and told me, 'Your group was one of the best Mod bands around in the '60s and '70s and your hit *Suburban Mod* is still a classic. I'm in the process of putting together a Road Show of that era – it will be countrywide and I want your band to be the headline act.'

Finding band members after nearly 40 years for a national tour

is a challenge. We're now in our sixties. Were the other members
still alive and did they want to go back on the road to ride the
wave of nostalgia, hitting the country at this particular time?
Would all the characters in the previous books still be around?
Penny's baby, Robin, was now in his thirties – was he looking for
his father?

The Sixties Boys on Tour, dare I say it, is a moving and light-
hearted story of the lives and loves of ageing Mods, their families
and friends as they attempt to hit the road again…